JOURNEY TO THE
ECSTATIC SELF

A WORKBOOK FOR SETTLING INTO YOUR SKIN, CULTIVATING AUTHENTICITY, AND RECONNECTING WITH YOUR RADIANT SELF

KAELAN STROUSE

ECSTATIC SELF
PRESS

Copyright

ISBN Hardcover: 978-1-7354689-0-7
ISBN Paperback: 978-1-7354689-2-1
ISBN EBook: 978-1-7354689-1-4

Library of Congress Control Number: 2020914185

Cover design by Alfred Obare
Typeset by Predra6art
Edited by Kayli Baker
Author photograph by Tuan Bui

Printed in the United States of America.

First printing, 2020.

Published by Ecstatic Self Press
Washington, D.C., USA.

www.ecstaticself.com

for Anthony, always

Table of Contents

Please visit ecstaticself.com for FREE bonus content
including paired audio recordings, videos, and additional
reading materials.

JOURNEY TO THE
ECSTATIC SELF

A WORKBOOK FOR SETTLING INTO YOUR SKIN, CULTIVATING AUTHENTICITY, AND RECONNECTING WITH YOUR RADIANT SELF

KAELAN STROUSE

Introduction:

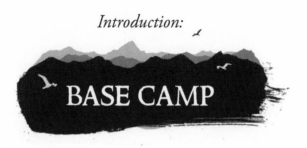

BASE CAMP

"To be nobody but yourself in a world which is doing its best day and night to make you like everybody else means to fight the hardest battle which any human being can fight and never stop fighting."
— E.E. Cummings, poet

P erhaps you're like me.

Perhaps you, too, grew up feeling like your body was an awkward machine that you couldn't fully operate. Your spirit didn't seem to fit within the boundaries of your skin. You felt clunky, uncouth, and perpetually ill at ease.

Maybe you, too, felt disconnected from your peers and the world around you. There were times when you sat on the concrete edges of an asphalt lot and stared in wonder at your classmates. You didn't understand why they enacted the games or swapped the stories that they did. You felt like an alien visitor, capable of comprehending their language but not able to follow the logic. What seemed to matter most to them meant nothing to you—and vice versa.

Perhaps, as an adult, you've found yourself in crowded rooms— totally alone—everyone else seeming to enjoy themselves except you.

Too much noise, too many bodies. You feel self-conscious and claustrophobic—pressed-in from all sides. You notice yourself silently judging everyone: that person is too tall, that one too short. She's so beautiful, but he's too slender. That guy has hair plugs, that girl is obnoxiously overdressed, and that fella needs to lock up his tweezers.

A mirror unexpectedly flashes your reflection back at you, and you shift the running critique to yourself. Your posture, your complexion, the stupid duck-face expression that you're making, how your clothes are insufficiently crisp (you should never have sat down on the subway, you realize). Your waist is too wide, your chest is too narrow, and you're two-weeks past needing to get your hair re-colored.

Trying to fix yourself, you lower your lids to make bedroom eyes, clench your jaw, and pout your lips even further. If you choose to make eye contact with anyone, it is only for long enough to convey dominance, attraction, dismissal, or amusement.

You wander to a corner to cocoon yourself in blessed darkness, and you notice that your collarbones are slick with sweat. Your heart is pounding. You realize that no matter how well you may have sized-up everyone in a bid to ease your own anxiety, it's not enough. You still feel uncomfortable and self-conscious. No facade you construct is ever enough to give you the sense of control and invulnerability that you crave.

You struggle to find a lasting feeling of belonging or security—here or anywhere. You are chronically aware that there are always others who are fitter, more beautiful, more powerful, or more talented to make you feel diminished. You are emotionally exhausted from this social gathering—your brain has been working at top-speed to process a barrage of chemical triggers. All of your fears and longings keep circling back to one, relentless belief that haunts you.

I am not enough.

I am not as handsome as my favorite actor; I do not have the body of that fitness model I idolize. I'm not as smart as Shakespeare or as talented as Mozart. I am not as wealthy as Bezos, as charismatic as Jackie, or as selfless as Teresa. I am unworthy. I am unlovable. I am inadequate in so many ways.

I don't want to be me.

Fleeing the crowded room, you seek some sort of salve to assuage the mounting panic and unworthiness inside. You pull up your favorite social media app and post a scandalous photo to see how many hearts you'll garner. You reach into your bag and withdraw a bottle of something medicinal. Maybe you text a friend to have them distract you—or scroll for somebody nearby, available to fuck. Perhaps you hit "order" on that designer handbag you've been eyeing but cannot afford—retail therapy, you assure yourself.

If you're like me, there's a nagging sense in your core that you are deficient. If only you could find the right diet/wardrobe/career/car/ partner—one day, you would no longer feel this inner lack. You live for a blessed point in the future where you will finally feel worthy, accepted, and beautiful. You long to belong to something.

If you're further into your journey, like I am now, you've come to realize that no amount of external validation will give you lasting self-worth. Sure, the applause and the "likes" can numb your angst for a short while—but the chasm of insecurity grows.

You may have thought that gaining ten thousand followers would finally provide fulfillment—but it didn't. You then wondered if one hundred thousand would—but that goalpost also came and went without providing lasting relief. You pondered if, instead of being a size two, a double zero would finally allow you permission to accept yourself—but it didn't.

I have spent most of my life searching for comfort within my skin. No bottle, no gym membership, no career success has ever given me the ability to truly love myself and find home inside. The more that I tried to be the person others would desire or applaud, the more disassociated I became—the more I didn't know who I was.

Through much trial, error, and internal questioning—as well as a tremendous amount of assistance from generous souls along the way—I have learned to find footholds in the rock-face of ecstatic self-hood. I have been reorienting away from seeking external approval and, instead, discovered that I am worthy as I am. More than that, I am an indelible, radiant spirit—and so is each person. I have unearthed a vast internal terrain of spiritual knowing and corporeal embodiment that has led me back to myself.

The routes toward selfhood that I've trod have been winding and wondrous. At times, they have led to majestic mountaintop vistas that have left me breathless. At other points, they have carried me to fearful precipices and have demanded that I jump into swirling, lightless abysses. These pathways have guided me into mystical forests, charred chaparrals, and butterfly-filled meadows.

I'm going to be honest: the journey to ecstatic selfhood has sometimes been terrifying. My fears have come at me like clawed branches scratching at stormy skies, foggy bogs sucking at my soles, and deep crags out of which I never expected to climb. I've had to abandon cherished dreams in order to ascend toward my destination. I have grieved—I have celebrated—I've danced in wild ecstasy, naked before the full moon and a bonfire of awakenings.

If you are like me—a fellow journeyer into the realms of the soul—then I offer you this book. It is a compass to help orient you along the trails and trials that lie ahead. Through the exercises and stories I share in these chapters, we will become spiritual travelers together.

I am by no means a perfect guide who has reached his final destination—I am very much still walking the path toward embodied selfhood. I have good days and poor—I still feel the rain and chilling winds. Furthermore, I do not claim to be a master cartographer of the self like others who have ascended to the pinnacles of academia and research in efforts to explore the frontiers of self-understanding. This book is solely a reflection of my personal journey, which I hope will be helpful to others. I offer the vantages I've glimpsed, the forks in the road I've chosen, and the footpaths that I've tried to bring me back to myself.

I gratefully acknowledge the expertise of those forebears who plotted the courses toward self-understanding that I've trod. I have learned so much from many wise-women, teachers, guides, and gurus—and through the collation of my studies and experiences, I believe I have accumulated knowledge that is valuable to share with others. I am not a therapist, a psychological counselor, a shaman, or an enlightened bodhisattva—but I am someone who has been wandering the trenches for many years. I approach this topic with both humanity and humility—sharing the guideposts I've marked to whomever it may be of use.

Coming into wholeness isn't a quick jaunt. I began this journey when I was a teenager. Back then, I desperately wanted to be someone other than my true self. I became a professional actor to escape my body and inhabit the minds of characters I preferred. Then, I fled the modern world and moved into a yogic ashram in a bid to outpace my longings and carnal desires. I tried to make myself into someone impenetrable and inhuman.

Since then, I have begun to learn the simple joy of being me—to sit alone and genuinely enjoy being with myself. I have discovered the satisfaction of embracing my imperfections, finding beauty in what is not pretty, and peace amidst the ruckus. I have been cultivating a life that I profoundly relish.

Over the past several years, I have developed a sense of belonging inside myself and amongst people for whom I care—to give and receive love. My life is far more fulfilling than I ever imagined it could be, but it looks almost nothing like what I dreamt it would be when I was younger. I have had to peel off layers of determined expectations to reveal my essence. I have had to let go of who I thought I needed to be in order to permit the real me to shine through.

If this speaks to you—the idea of a journey to know and accept your ecstatic, integrated, joyful self—then grab some boots, because we've got some winding, curious, glorious paths ahead of us. Strap in!

"The big question is whether you are going to be able to say a hearty yes to your adventure."
— **Joseph Campbell, professor of literature and mythology**

Quiz:

GEAR CHECK

Who doesn't love a personality test, eh? I bet your internet browsing history says that you do.

Simple enough: for the statements below, circle either "True" or "False" based on what you most-often experience currently. There are no right or wrong answers—so be honest. No one is going to see the results but you.

1. When I find myself alone with nothing to do, I feel anxious. *True — False*
2. When friends invite me out to dinner, I get nervous thinking about what I am going to talk about. *True — False*
3. It takes me a long time to get dressed. I frequently change my outfit until I find the appropriate look. *True — False*
4. If people close to me were to offer a description of who they know me to be, it would closely align with how I would describe myself. *True — False*
5. I would rather have the life of a character from my favorite story than my own. *True — False*

6. I frequently check my reflection or take selfies to make certain that my appearance is exactly right. *True — False*

7. I hear the sound of my voice—or even just my laugh—in a recording and think it sounds fake. *True — False*

8. I practice how to pose for pictures—I only want to be photographed with a specific expression, from a particular angle. *True — False*

9. I will not post pictures online without first cleaning them up in Photoshop. *True — False*

10. I have a compulsive habit regarding my external appearance (examples: picking at acne, getting a weekly haircut, washing my car at the first sign of dirt). *True — False*

11. I have a strong desire to achieve perfection (in my work, my body, etc.). *True — False*

12. I have friendships with people who know and love the "real me." *True — False*

13. I am the same person, regardless of whom I am interacting with. *True — False*

14. I shape-shift to become the person someone wants me to be. *True — False*

15. I regularly take time to examine both the motives behind my actions and the reasoning behind my beliefs. *True — False*

16. I find it easy to both give and accept gestures of love from others through kind words, touch, or actions. *True — False*

17. I enjoy making eye contact with others, seeing and being seen myself. *True — False*

18. It doesn't intimidate me to stand alone at the front of a room and declare my beliefs. *True — False*

19. I can be vulnerable and share my authentic self with those who have earned my trust. *True — False*

20. I don't over-share. I have healthy boundaries and don't confuse over-exposure with genuine connection. *True — False*

21. I have people who I sincerely trust, and they trust me. *True — False*

22. I feel like I can rely on myself, regardless of the intensity of the challenges I face. *True — False*

23. I genuinely like the people I spend time with. They feed me in an emotional, mental, or spiritual capacity. *True — False*

24. I am generally honest. I don't use white lies or lying by omission. *True — False*

25. I frequently notice myself changing facts to showcase myself in the best light. *True — False*

26. I can confidently explore both physical and emotional intimacy. I enjoy both the animalistic and spiritual sides of sex. *True — False*

27. I am comfortable with my body. It causes me no undue stress to be naked in a locker room, in front of a partner, or in another socially appropriate setting. *True — False*

28. If disaster struck today, I know I would make it through. I have confidence in myself to survive and remain optimistic. *True — False*

29. I have unexpected and inexplicable bouts of rage in response to small, seemingly benign stimuli. *True — False*

30. There are specific emotions I don't express—such as anger, sorrow, or compassion. *True — False*

31. I spend a great deal of energy curating an idealized online presence so people will think well of me. *True — False*

32. The desire to have my body conform to a specific standard motivates my daily food choices and how I spend much of my time. *True — False*

33. No matter how fit or thin I might be, I never feel like it's quite enough. If I were just a little leaner or more toned, I'd be happier. *True — False*

34. How others will perceive my life-choices is more important to me than the actual happiness I will derive from my decisions. *True — False*

35. I maintain significant expenses that are beyond my means to reasonably support (ex: sports car, luxury home, extensive designer wardrobe). *True — False*

How did these questions make you feel? Were some of them uncomfortable? If so, you are not alone. It can be unnerving to examine ideas that poke at our current discomfort.

When you are ready, please use this key to assess your response:

If you marked "True" to questions 1-3, 5-11, 14, 25, 29-35, give yourself one point for each. If you marked "False" to questions: 4, 12-13, 15-24, 26-28, give yourself one point for each.

Total number of "points" _____ out of a possible of 35.

I wish I could give you a range that says that zero to eight points means "You are doing great!" and twenty-four to thirty points means "Get yourself to an emergency room right now—you are about to explode from self-hate!" But I can't.

The truth is: more than even a couple of points suggests that you're currently maintaining a high level of disconnection from your inner self. Any points are unfavorable. This is not a chastisement of you as a person—it just means that you probably have some growth-work to do. But then, so do we all.

I also want to offer that a high score might be a reflection of short-term, unusual levels of stress in your life. Taken a week or two from now, perhaps you might have scored much lower. Contrarily, elevated points might also be an indicator of needing to seek out medical or professional guidance. This book can be a valuable resource on your healing journey, but one-on-one coaching from a licensed therapist can be an immensely useful tool.

Even if you don't go the psychological route, having a mentor, a village elder, a pastor, a healer, or someone practiced in helping others toward wholeness can be invaluable. Consider reaching out to people in your network to find out what they're doing to keep themselves emotionally and mentally well. Remember that asking for help is never weakness—even the bravest need support sometimes. Real courage is exploring to one's limits and then being carried by someone the rest of the way. We are social animals—we need one another to survive. We'll only make it so far on our own.

With this in mind, let's begin.

Chapter 1:

THE
ADVENTURE BEGINS

"The greatest gift you ever give is your honest self."
— **Fred Rogers, television personality**

I was standing in a skin-tight, black leotard—in the middle of an acting class, during my sophomore year at Northwestern University—when something clicked into place inside my head. I suddenly understood that I didn't really want to be studying acting. I didn't care about Chekhov or Molière—I had little interest in becoming a versatile, gritty, chameleon-like actor. Instead, I realized that what brought me to this school was a desire to become one of the most iconic characters in American cinema, to play him so thoroughly that the boundaries between him and I would blur. I had chosen to pursue the career of a professional actor because what I really wanted was to be cast as the Dark Knight. I wanted to become Batman.

Now, almost every child plays at being a superhero at somepoint in their life. When we are young, we have so little agency to make decisions or protect ourselves—everyone makes choices for us and holds power over us. But by donning the cape of a hero, children feel empowered. A vigilante's mask gives a child the belief that they can exert a modicum control in a world where adults rule. They gain a sense of strength and security through role play.

Additionally, superheroes lack complexity—the good guys are universally virtuous, and the bad guys are unanimously cold-hearted criminals (at least in the mainstream, made-for-television, cartoon adaptations that played on cable in my youth). They provide a world of absolutes that are easy for developing brains to comprehend. There's little nuance or conflicting motivations.

As most of us age, however, we generally start to appreciate the complexity of more sophisticated stories. We go to high school and read Dostoevsky, Shakespeare, William Golding—or even start exploring the graphic novel versions of our heroes, which are generally much deeper. We learn to appreciate human foibles, discombobulated and conflicting desires, world views that don't exist in black and white, but in gradations of gray. We start to appreciate in others—and ourselves—the messiness inherent in living. This growing refinement is a natural part of psychological maturation.

So, what was wrong with me? Why was I—around nineteen-years-old, at this point—so thoroughly drawn to a flattened superhero identity that I not only wanted to inhabit the character of Batman, but I wanted to become him? Why would I choose a duotone life over the vibrant technicolor of my reality?

To explore this question, let's examine the character of Batman as I knew him. He seemed rugged, unapproachable, and enigmatic. A man's man—what might be described as a conservative's view of contemporary masculinity. In his daytime life, he is the suave billionaire, Bruce Wayne. He drives fast cars, has dispensable women hanging on his arm, and is a generous philanthropist. He is solitary, rakish, and successful—powerful, without letting anyone get too close.

At night, Bruce dons a cape and cowl and ventures into Gotham to save its hapless citizens. He never gets hurt in any debilitating way (in the cable cartoon version, at least), he can do whatever he wants, and he's pretty universally adored. He attains a sort of God-like status—swinging high above the masses below.

For myself—someone who felt immensely insecure with himself and his identity—Bruce/Batman felt like a comforting trope. He is the modern-day cowboy—what many boys are told they should aspire to be. Young men are encouraged to bury their emotions, embody strength, and never let anyone hold them down. As someone who was scared of who I was, this persona of Batman seemed like a suitable replacement for a genuine sense of self. After all, who wouldn't want to be friends with Batman? He's a badass. Being him promised to make me secure and happy, which was far from the dissatisfaction I perpetually felt.

But, this idea of Batman being an appealing persona doesn't really hold up to scrutiny. When we examine the emotional life of this caped crusader, we observe that Bruce is a sad and isolated man who is haunted by visions of his parents' untimely death. He lives alone in an empty mansion with only a butler for company (at least until Robin and the others show up, years later). It is a lonely existence that shouldn't be wished upon anyone. He has few he can trust—no one with whom he can truly be vulnerable or intimate. He has more money than he could ever need, but he is miserable. He is haunted by the ghosts from his past and his own feelings of insufficiency—his inability to save his parents.

Why on earth would I want to adopt this persona and abandon my genuine self? What was I running from? Why would I rather become a neurotic loner with a savior complex than a beautiful and complex version of the real me? Because, shit. That bat dude is messed up.

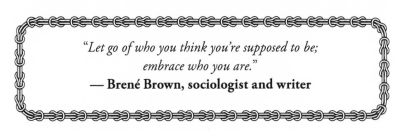

"Let go of who you think you're supposed to be; embrace who you are."
— **Brené Brown, sociologist and writer**

Up through my mid-twenties, being me was painful. I felt intensely vulnerable, overly sensitive, and unable to relate to other young men and women. In elementary and middle school, I was routinely picked on for being too effeminate, for processing information differently than other kids, for being compassionate in a way that was at odds with the insect mutilation that regularly happened on playground blacktops. In short, I was queer, neurodivergent, and crushingly empathetic—I could feel emotions to a painfully heightened degree.

All of this combined to make me feel that I was made incorrectly. I wasn't man-enough, tough-enough, powerful-enough. I wondered if there was something wrong with my brain that prevented me from seeing the world in the same way as everyone else. I chronically felt overwhelmed by my fellow students and their emotions—their taunts, jeers, and jokes. Being intensely empathetic, I tried to numb my awareness, block-off my emotional sensitivity—which, in turn, drove a greater wedge between me and my peers because I then seemed even more distant. I desperately hoped that if I could become someone different—if I could inhabit a persona of which the rest of the world would better approve—then maybe my discomfort would abate. Maybe I would finally feel accepted and wanted.

And who was the most beloved, the most macho, the most secure character that I could pick from? Batman, of course. Nothing ever got to him—he was a stud. I began hitting the gym, lowering my voice, and swaggering my walk. Without consciously being aware of what I was doing, I began to cover over the real me with the trappings of an identity that I thought others would better appreciate. In the process, I became achingly disconnected internally.

When I would hear my voice on a recording, I wouldn't recognize it. When I would laugh, I would wonder who was making the noise I heard. My smile felt awkward and forced. In the rare instances where I would experience physical touch with another person, it would feel dangerous—as if they could feel the papier-mâché enveloping my skin. I became a two-dimensional cutout of what I thought I was supposed to be.

As I grew older and my disconnection grew more profound, my internal levels of anxiety climbed. The possibility that anyone would be able to peer through my disguise provided great distress. I strove to make my mask thicker, more elaborate. I crafted a persona so complete that I no longer knew that it wasn't who I really was—I buried my truth from myself. All that I was cognizant of was a longing for connection in the world while simultaneously feeling myself being held back from it.

I became a professional actor because I thought that if I could become universally revered—if I could become a Hollywood heartthrob and get cast in the biggest roles (like Batman)—maybe then I would finally feel like I was good-enough, like I was worthy. So I tried harder, did everything within my power to make that dream a reality. I took countless acting classes, hired a forgettable number of trainers, and controlled my diet with a fanatical level of devotion.

If I had been very unlucky, I would have ended up with the life for which I was craving. I would have ended up in the Hollywood hills with an A-list manager, a flush bank account, and a shelf of awards. And if all of that had manifested, I am pretty certain that I would have also ended up with a one-way ticket to my untimely death. If I had climbed all the way to the top of the echelons of achievement and still found a pit of dissatisfaction gnawing inside me, what other choice would I have had but to take the leap? If being a star didn't make me happy—then nothing would.

We see it all the time: celebrities who climb the ladders of success searching for validation, searching for acceptance and belonging, only to careen back down and leave a crater in their wake. Robin Williams, Phillip Seymour Hoffman, River Phoenix, Marilyn Monroe—the list goes on and on. Stars who plummeted to earth. Even the heavens couldn't provide them with wellbeing or genuine happiness. In many instances, the strain of celebrity status made their psychological imbalances more unmanageable.

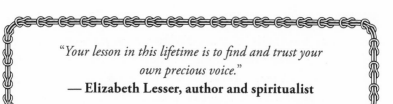

Fortunately for me, I didn't get what I wanted. I graduated college and launched my career as a professional actor—and proceeded to struggle. Most days, I felt like a runner repeatedly sprinting into a wall at top speed. I routinely watched people who I worked harder than, who I felt I was more talented than, get offered opportunities of which I only dreamt. I repeatedly received feedback that I was a great second or third choice for a role—but there was just something about me that read as inauthentic. Casting directors flat-out told me that I was posing rather than really living. Actors are lauded for their ability to connect and reveal their humanity—I couldn't do that. Instead of stripping down, I kept armoring up.

"[Self] love comes when manipulation stops," says psychologist Joyce Brothers. "When you dare to reveal yourself fully. When you dare to be vulnerable." The feeling of failure in my career—of nose-diving repeatedly—eventually drove me to turn my focus inward in self-inquiry. My non-abating dissatisfaction forced me to carefully examine the facade that I had unknowingly built during my uncomfortable years. Brick by brick, stone by stone, I began the process of dismantling the walls of my forged identity. Meditation, sessions with healers and elders, mindful self-inquiry, journaling, art creation, and various modalities of therapy revealed the character that I had erected to hide my truth. I began to expose my vulnerable self beneath the plaster molding.

Over the course of this excavation, I began to forge authentic relationships for the first time in my life—meaningful friendships, tender partnerships, human bonds. I learned to stop seeking stamps of approval from the outside world and instead cultivate self-worth within. I began to understand how no amount of success, fitness, wealth or beauty would ever give me a sense of lasting security—and that if I lived my life solely for the approval of others, I would remain heartbroken, disillusioned, and chronically disappointed.

I started to discover that the quiet simplicity of being myself was one of the greatest joys that life could provide. In time, I found my soulmate, adopted a rescue dog, and gave up searching for outward acclaim. I pursued a path that made me feel contented—even if no one else would understand or approve. I discovered that lasting happiness involved a rocking chair on a quiet evening, a dusky sunset filled with fireflies, and the warm embrace of a partner who loves me with all my imperfections. I quit the rat-race—I jumped off the hamster wheel. I began to live for my joy.

How many of us grow up feeling that it is unsafe to be ourselves, that we'd rather become someone else? How many of us abandon our personal truth in order to gain approval, social capital, acceptance, or power? How many disconnect from inner worth and instead seek the appearance of strength, normality, and perfection? We cash in our humanity and trade it in for societal approval. What we build to maintain that approval comes to feel increasingly less like a cozy nest and more like a prison.

Perhaps there was a point in your life where you decided it was unacceptable to just be you. Maybe one of your parents doubted their own self-worth and pressured you to provide their life with meaning. Perhaps you grew up surrounded by substance abuse and wanted to prove how you've flourished despite it. Maybe you grew up realizing that you were different from everyone else because of your gender identity, sexuality, or neurological wiring. Maybe you were told that you were unlovable because of something you could not change.

For whatever reason, you might have learned that being you was a liability. To compensate, you strove extra hard to get all A's, get the lead in the class play, or become the captain of the varsity softball team. Perhaps you spent years at the gym squatting for the idealized body. Maybe you pushed yourself so hard that you burned out or broke down—or turned to sex, drugs, social media, or any of the dozens of other forms of self-medication we have available to take the sting out of living. We have tried to numb those parts that keep scratching us in the night, whispering that something isn't quite right inside of us. The voices that hiss that we aren't living our best lives.

It is time to ponder these questions: who do you think you are, deep down? How does the persona you project match the identity of you at your core?

EXERCISE

Using just a few sentences, write out how you believe certain groups of people would describe you.

The world sees me as:

_____

_____

_____

_____

_____

Take a moment and reread what you wrote. How does it feel? Do you feel like you named the "crux" of you—the meaty, central bit that really gets to the core of who you are? Let's try again—this time, I want you to answer the question: how would you describe yourself to your closest friend? Hopefully, this answer will be a little more intimate.

My closest loved one sees me as:

_____

_____

_____

_____

Did we get a little closer? Read it again and notice the differences compared with what you wrote the first time. Let's go even a bit deeper. Now I want you to describe your identity as if no one else will ever read it. If your self-description were locked in a treasure chest and dropped to the bottom of the sea, what would you write?

In my secret world, I am:

_____

_____

_____

_____

_____

Was that any closer to your truth? You might find that only some elements of all three descriptions are true, they could all be the same—or, you might find that none of them are quite right. Whatever your experience is of this exercise, I promise that it's perfectly alright. This is the beginning of a long journey, and these are but the first few steps.

> "Knowing others is intelligent. Knowing yourself is enlightened. Conquering others takes force. Conquering yourself is true strength."
> — **Tao Te Ching by Lao Tzu**

My greatest joy in being an actor was getting to be different—to shed my exterior and feel confident, sexy, or just someone else altogether. Acting gave me applause from an audience, approval from casting directors when they offered me roles, and the high of feeling special and chosen. But these experiences were not what I most needed to establish lasting self-worth. I needed to accept myself for being beautiful and worthy, even without the glamour or recognition. I needed to learn how to form genuine, meaningful connections with others, I needed to cultivate self-love, and learn how to exchange love with others. But I was purposefully pursuing a career that provided external, rather than internal, rewards.

Hopefully, you have made life choices (with your profession, say) that provide you with intrinsic joy. Intrinsic joy means that you derive satisfaction from the act of doing, as opposed to the approval of others. For example, going for a bike ride because you love the sensation of freedom—the wind whipping your hair, the smell of freshly-cut grass, the weightless experience of flight—that's intrinsic joy. By contrast, if you ride a bike because your primary motivation is to impress other people with your wheelies and looking like a badass, that is extrinsic joy.

When we make our choices with extrinsic motivations, we become overly fixated on what others will think or say about us. We place our worth in the hands of others—will they approve of us or not? Extrinsically motivated decision making might look like buying a new jacket that we cannot afford, but we fear that we will be social outcasts without the latest style. It's ordering unappetizing food because it photographs well and will earn some double-taps online, even if we find it appalling.

Just to compare, imagine purchasing a fuzzy sweater that reminds you of a teddy bear you had as a child—that's an intrinsically motivated choice. It is ordering your favorite meal, calories be damned, and relishing every bite. You feel ebullient—and it really doesn't matter what anyone else thinks or says. Obviously, no choice is going to be purely intrinsic or extrinsic, but we need to be aware of the balance between the two.

Interestingly enough, people who are able to make intrinsically aligned choices are the ones we describe as having a "strong sense of self." They know what they want and go after it—critics be damned. They are the trailblazers, the innovators, and the harbingers of change. They are the sort of people I admire and aspire to emulate.

> "Great spirits have always encountered violent opposition from mediocre minds. The mediocre mind is incapable of understanding the man who refuses to bow blindly to conventional prejudices and chooses instead to express his opinions courageously and honestly."

— Albert Einstein, atomic scientist and watchmaker

EXERCISE

What are experiences in life that provide you with great joy? By narrowing in on things that make you light up inside, you may gain a clearer picture of what matters most to you—and, by extension, your most essential self. Again, focus on the things that make you feel genuinely satisfied, regardless of who else is watching. What would you choose to do every day, if you could?

Activities that bring me deep joy:

_____

_____

_____

_____

_____

_____

_____

_____

_____

_____

_____

> *"My mission in life is not merely to survive, but to thrive; and to do so with some passion, some compassion, some humor, and some style."*
> **— Maya Angelou, poet and author**

If you are going to accept your real self, you have to get past what other people will think about who you are. Yes, the opinions of those to whom you are closest will always matter—yes, we will forever have people to whom we are accountable. But if we are only living for the benefit of others' opinions, it will be a struggle to find lasting satisfaction. The whims and perspectives of other people will matter more than our own happiness.

Perhaps you have already made significant, life-changing decisions that can't easily be thrown off or altered. Your spouse, the house you live in, the car you drive. Did you make those choices because you thought they'd bring you lasting joy, or because it was the thing that you were expected to do? It's not necessary to alter those decisions right now—but it is important to become aware of why you did what you did.

> *"I do not care so much what I am to others as I care what I am to myself."*
> **— Michel de Montaigne, Renaissance philosopher**

Let's rank some of our major life choices on a spectrum ranging from fully intrinsic to entirely extrinsic. Go ahead and mark wherever you feel like your decisions most accurately exist between the two extremes.

Significant Other(s)

On the far left, you have a partner who you always adore spending time with, they make you feel good when you're around them, and you feel like you have some sort of "soul connection." On the far right, it's a significant other who you chose because you thought your mother would approve of them, your friends like them, or they were great arm-candy. Perhaps you felt like they would help you better fit into society or give you financial security.

Fully Intrinsic - - - - - - - - - - - - - - - - Fully Extrinsic

Career

This time, to the left we have a career that you wake up each morning and can't wait to engage with. It's a career that fills you with passion, makes you believe that you are creating a positive impact in the world, and helps you achieve your life's mission. On the far right is a career path that you took because it infers status or social capital. Perhaps you thought it would make people envious of you, give you lots of money, or look good on a resumé—but you don't derive any inherent joy in the doing of it.

Fully Intrinsic - - - - - - - - - - - - - - - - Fully Extrinsic

Home

The far left represents a home that allows you to relax as soon as you walk in. Everything there has a purpose, sparks a memory that makes you smile. You find that the only objects that belong in your home are things that you personally value (even if they have little monetary worth)—your home brings you a sense of solace and sanctuary. The right-hand side indicates a home that doesn't align with your values. Maybe it's impressive, but you personally don't find the design or layout appealing—you walk in, and you feel tenser than when you arrived. Perhaps it is cluttered with items you don't actually need but feel like you should hold onto.

Fully Intrinsic - - - - - - - - - - - - - - - - Fully Extrinsic

Closest Friendships

If you circle somewhere toward the left, your primary friendships provide you with great joy; you feel like you can be you and can share anything with them, let your guard fully down. These people provide a sense of home and belonging. They don't require anything from you in order to continue your good standing with them—they'll love you no matter what you give/do/say. On the far right, these are friendships that are conditional—they will only profess to care about you if you say or do the correct thing. These are friendships that you cannot fully trust, that you feel like you don't know the core of each person. These would also be friendships with people who are beautiful or impressive, but they don't add any tangible benefit to your life beyond social standing.

Fully Intrinsic - - - - - - - - - - - - - - - - Fully Extrinsic

Car/Mode of Transportation

On the left, you have a vehicle that gets you around, that you enjoy, and is within your means. Maybe the mode of transport you use has some inherited sentimental value or is a lot of fun to ride/drive. The right side is a car that you cannot easily afford, that you purchased to feel more cool/confident/get you laid.

Fully Intrinsic - - - - - - - - - - - - - - - - - Fully Extrinsic

Take a moment to reflect on your answers. Feel free to jot down any observations in the space below.

_____

_____

_____

_____

_____

_____

_____

_____

> *"No amount of self-improvement can make up for any lack of self-acceptance."*
> — **Robert Holden, psychologist**

While there were countless moments in my time as an actor where I felt intrinsic joy—overnight film shoots joking around with my co-stars, exploring a meaty script that tested my artistic limits, hashing out scenes until they felt emotionally resonant—these moments were far and few between. Most of my days were spent attempting to claw worthiness from the approval of others.

The funny thing is—if you had asked me at that time if I was happy in my life choices, if I derived joy from being an actor—I would have enthusiastically said yes. I couldn't really appreciate how unhappy I was, how I was pursuing status symbols, living for a mythical day in the future where I would finally feel worthy.

Almost like any addiction that develops slowly, you don't initially realize that you're in a rough place. Many people with eating disorders don't necessarily recognize that they're starving themselves until one day they wake up and notice that all they've recently eaten has been a saltine cracker and a cube of cheese. You cannot always see your own disconnection or unhappiness—it can both sneak up and be masked by the neon glow of aspirations for the future.

That glorious day that you're fighting for—the day where all your dreams come to fruition, and you are finally fulfilled—will never arrive. Being Batman will not make you whole.

Let me be clear about this: even if you somehow manage to fight your way all the way to the golden ring you so desperately sought—become Bruce Wayne—you will eventually realize that the external goal doesn't have the depth or richness that you hoped it would. That thing you attained won't make you finally feel worthwhile or satisfied. It will seem flat and hollow compared to your expectations of it. To keep moving forward, to keep having something to fight for—a new goal to instill a sense of purpose and hope—you will have to dream more audaciously.

Being a movie star didn't give you long-term satisfaction? Well, maybe winning an Emmy will. You got the Emmy, and it didn't change things? Well, that's because it wasn't an Academy Award—those are the *real* big deal. Suddenly, you've got three Oscars sitting on a shelf in the bathroom and a suicide note tucked into your desk drawer—just in case—because, no matter how much acclaim you collect, you're still miserable. You're still not fulfilled. You still don't want to be where you are, in your skin, living your own life.

Actor Jim Carrey said, "I think everybody should get rich and famous and do everything they ever dreamed of so they can see that it's not the answer." There's a term for reaching your long-held aspirations and finding out how disappointing they actually are—it's called "the arrival fallacy." You climb to the top of the mountain and discover that view is polluted and hazy. You win the award, only to find that it's made of plastic and held together with craft glue. A deep sadness sets in when you suddenly know the thing you fought so hard to achieve—that goal that was supposed to give your life meaning—is actually hollow and powerless to make you truly happy.

Furthermore, the desire to be extraordinary—the desire to leave behind a normal life and trade it in for glittering trophies and a few brief moments in the spotlight—can underlie mental health issues. When being yourself as you are is not good enough, what does that say about your human experience as a whole? Why do you have to aspire toward greatness?

"Those who put up the skyscrapers, write the bestselling books, perform on stage, or make partner may, in fact, be the unwell ones. Whereas those characters who—without agony—can bear an ordinary life, the so-called 'mediocrities,' may in fact be the emotional superstars, the aristocrats of spirit, the captains of the heart. The world divides into the privileged who can be ordinary, and the damned compelled to be remarkable," says philosopher Alain de Botton.

Modern sociologist and lecturer, Brené Brown, writes, "When I look at narcissism through the vulnerability lens, I see the shame-based fear of being ordinary. I see the fear of never feeling extraordinary enough to be noticed, to be lovable, to belong, or to cultivate a sense of purpose." She goes on to add, "Because true belonging only happens when we present our authentic, imperfect selves to the world, our sense of belonging can never be greater than our level of self-acceptance. [...] Let go of who you think you're supposed to be; embrace who you are."

The point of all this is: are you happy as you are right now? I'm not asking about the external stuff—the stuff that changes with the flow of time—like having a specific income or romantic partner. I'm asking if you genuinely like being you? Your true, essential self? If an asteroid flew out of the Kuiper belt and careened directly into the shiny object of your infatuation, the thing you've been coveting—would you be okay? If you found out that you'll never achieve all the things you hope for, would you be happy? Would you like yourself without any trappings of success?

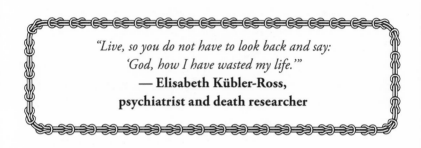

"Live, so you do not have to look back and say:
'God, how I have wasted my life.'"
— Elisabeth Kübler-Ross,
psychiatrist and death researcher

"I want to know if you can be alone with yourself, and if you truly like the company you keep in the empty moments," says Oriah Mountain Dreamer in her poem, "The Invitation." Do you like who you sit with when you're all alone? Is there a part of you that thinks, "If people knew who I really am inside, they would reject me," or "I am unlovable," or even "I am a monster?"

Snapchat filters, Photoshop, and low-key lighting are all examples of ways that we say, "This other version of me is better. I am imperfect as I actually am." We are covering up what makes us beautiful—our individualized spirits. We are hiding our quirks, our oddities, our imperfections—that which makes us unique and stunning to behold.

The fashion photographer, John Rankin Waddell, took studio portraits of fifteen teenagers and asked them to photoshop themselves before he shared the images publicly. He then placed the teens' pixel-tweaked portraits beside their raw, unaltered photographs and asked the students to reflect and compare. The teens universally commented that their modified versions looked less appealing—many had altered them so thoroughly that they appeared inhuman, almost alien-like. They morphed themselves outside the bounds of human-ness because they thought it would make them look more desirable. In seeing their un-Facetuned selves, they realized that there was beauty in their imperfections, acne, too-wide noses, and undefined jawlines.

Most of us are not given the opportunity to see ourselves from the outside as others see us. Most of us do not tangibly see how inhuman our idealized versions of ourselves are when compared to the genuine articles. Instead, too many of us spend our days plucking and prodding, tucking and squeezing our way through life—hiding whatever we think is unflattering.

My husband used to laugh because—for the longest time—I couldn't walk past a mirror without unconsciously changing how I held my face. I would lower my eyebrows, clench my jaw, and flare my nostrils. He would chuckle and call it my "mirror face." While it was an objectively flattering facial expression—it was not reflective of what I really looked like. I never used that expression in normal life, only in mirrors or photographs. It felt disingenuous. I have since diligently worked on smiling authentically at myself in mirrors—it is surprisingly challenging.

One of the first steps in our journey toward wholeness is to begin to notice all the myriad of ways we consciously or subconsciously send out the message, "I'd rather be someone else." It's time to start repeating a different credo. We need to affirm that "I am the best person I could possibly be. I am enough."

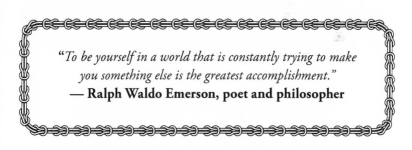

"To be yourself in a world that is constantly trying to make you something else is the greatest accomplishment."
— **Ralph Waldo Emerson, poet and philosopher**

I want to engage a more creative part of your brain. Please grab a pen, some chalk, colored markers, crayons, or anything to doodle with and get ready to color. I am going to have you do several sketches or paintings. This artwork doesn't need to be good—it just needs to exist.

Create a self-portrait of how you see yourself and your life currently. This doesn't have to be literal.

Do a self-portrait of how other people want you to be.

Do one of your idealized version of you.

Do a portrait of the happiest version of you.

Draw you as if you were looking through the eyes of someone who loved you to the depth of their soul.

Compare them all and try not to judge them too harshly. Journal your observations below.

_____

_____

_____

_____

_____

_____

_____

_____

SUMMARY:

— **Being yourself is perfect. There's no one else you need to (or can) be.**

— **Excessive external striving can be a sign of deep internal dissatisfaction.**

— **Focus on intrinsic joy rather than extrinsic validation.**

Chapter 2:

SERENE VISTAS AHEAD

*"I live in that solitude which is painful in youth,
but delicious in the years of maturity."*
— **Albert Einstein, atomic scientist and watchmaker**

B eing alone can be one of life's greatest curses or blessings, depending on your perspective. When approached from the correct vantage, solitude can provide us with time to turn inward, reflect, and connect with a truth that is often covered by the blaring qualities of life. If you want to reconnect with yourself, you may need to step away from the cacophony of the world and listen attentively within.

In today's world, we talk quite a bit about the word "psyche"—it is the prefix used to describe the psychologist leading your treatment sessions, the psychopharmacological practitioner prescribing your meds, the psychoanalyst shrinking your head. We assume that the word has an analytical, logic-focused derivation—psyche must be something that can be quantified, measured, or dissected, right?

Well, if you look at the etymology of the word, psyche actually translates from Greek to mean "soul" and "breath." Working with someone to more deeply uncover their authentic self is soulful work, and one of the best ways to ride our awareness inward is by hitching our minds to the flow of our breath. To come into wholeness requires relaxing into the breath—letting go of the tenseness that has kept the ribcage bound, so we may connect with our soul.

To know ourselves, we must dive into a deep, mysterious vortex of ideas, impressions, and observations that are seldom neat, orderly, or easily understood. Entering our psyches, we leave behind the land of logic, laws, and rationality to frolic in a dreamscape of flowing mist and myth. For us to make sense of that which is inside, we must connect with our breath and our spirit. We must learn to quiet the thought-waves of our mind and peer into the deeper waters of soulfulness.

Simply focusing on the shape, rhythm, and quality of your breath can reveal a great deal about your overall emotional state and mental health. Regular, steady breathing often indicates an evenness of mind, a settledness in one's body. Ragged, irregular breath can indicate imbalance, disease, discomfort. Shallow, frantic breathing can suggest panic or worry. Deep, flowing breathing can relate to feelings of contentment and ease in life. You can learn a lot about a person by observing how they respirate.

Have you ever noticed someone sitting nearby who keeps making loud exhalations like they're sighing? If you look over, perhaps they appear as if they are about to cry. But, if you were studying the sounds of their breathing, you could have already anticipated their distress. Perhaps there is someone across your office who is huffing and puffing frenetically, almost hyperventilating. You don't need to peer over your cubicle to know that they are stressed and reaching their capacity to manage their anxiety.

It can be discomforting to turn our focus inward to become aware of our breath and our psyches. We are so outwardly oriented in contemporary culture that turning inside can feel strange and foreign. Additionally, there are so many distractions. We have an endless variety of screens, videos, chat apps, social media to turn to and distract us from our inner states. Studies have shown that modern Americans are exposed to up to 10,000 pieces of advertising in a single day—the world is constantly pulling on our attention.[1]

For some, it can even feel frightening to become aware of what is going on inside. To become fully aware of one's thoughts, emotions, breath patterns is almost a heroic act—it requires a tremendous amount of courage and wherewithal. A study done by Timothy Wilson at the University of Virginia showed that around 67% of men would rather subject themselves to an electric shock than sit alone with their thoughts for fifteen minutes.[2] If you are unaccustomed to turning within, you may need to strap on your gladiator sandals and grab a helmet—intense fear can ignite when listening to your inner self for the first time. You are likely to discover buried emotions that you didn't know you felt—intense feelings that have been masked by being oriented outwardly.

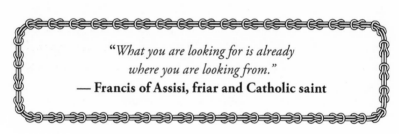

"What you are looking for is already
where you are looking from."
— **Francis of Assisi, friar and Catholic saint**

From the time I was little, I was fascinated with exploring my own thoughts. I would find myself spontaneously sitting in lotus pose and focusing inward, observing the comings and goings of my mind. I would imagine that the thought-streams in my head belonged to a foreign entity, and I was the observer of those ongoing ideas and opinions. It was years later that I discovered that this was actually a time-honored meditation technique.

I remember sitting in my desk in first grade, quietly observing the intake and outflow of my breath and feeling a rush of overwhelming ecstasy—it was as if the world was swirling around me in arcs of effervescent joy. I would repeatedly feel myself being swept away by this almost-orgasmic experience of deep breathing while my teacher droned on about counting and sea turtles. I didn't know that this was something unique to me—I assumed that my peers had the same ecstatic experiences happening to them.

I was aware, however, that I perceived the world in a very different way from my fellow students. I would sit on the sidelines at recess and wonder what was wrong with me—why did the jokes the other kids made, and their topics of conversation, seem so foreign and un-relatable? What interested them did not interest me—and vice versa. I asked my parents if I had a cognitive impairment of which they hadn't informed me—I felt so alone, so separated from the way everyone around me articulated their values and opinions of the world.

As I've gotten older, I've come to identify as neurodivergent—but at the time, I felt that the way my brain functioned was broken. I tried to suppress my identity and natural way of thinking in order to fit in with the world. Had there been some sort of mentor or guide to encourage me to continue on this path of deep breathing and self-inquiry, perhaps I wouldn't have needed to suffer so much as I grew older and entered my teenage years. Instead, I shut-off this innate self-awareness and grew further away from my essence.

It took until halfway through college before I began to rediscover mindfulness. I became interested in yoga and took classes in both the physical postures and meditational aspects. The summer before my senior year, I attended my first-ever meditation retreat—high up in the Rocky Mountains. For me, it was a feeling of coming home—a sense of reconnecting with my truth and uncovering parts of my self-understanding that I had lost during the progression into adolescence.

Since that time, I have explored meditation each morning and every evening. It has become the bedrock for understanding myself, my longings, and my identity. I would encourage you to cultivate a practice of your own. Without taking time to turn within and process the experiences of the day, it is difficult to live as our most present, settled, and accepting self.

> *"Meditation practice isn't about trying to throw ourselves away and become something better. It's about befriending who we are already."*
> — **Pema Chödrön, Buddhist nun and spiritual teacher**

There are parts of your mind that are pre-verbal. The amygdala, for example—the section of your brain that is responsible for the flight-or-fight response, that manages threats and stress—cannot tell you what it is thinking. It developed at an early time, evolutionarily speaking. Some scientists call it the "lizard brain."[3] It cannot make clear what it is responding to through words. So, if you are relying on your mind-chatter to articulate how you are actually feeling, you will have an incomplete picture of your mental and emotional state. You may be responding to something and not entirely understand why.

How often have we seen ourselves or someone else become agitated and not even be cognizant of it? We suddenly find ourselves flinging a coffee mug across the room or welling up with tears. If someone were to inquire why, it would take a few attempts to accurately articulate our distress. All we know is that we've been instigated in some way—some intangible catalyst set us off. This is an example of our lizard brain, the amygdala, taking control and co-opting parts of the rational, decision-making parts of our minds. We quite literally cannot think straight once the amygdala gets involved—and it cannot clearly tell us why it's slamming on the acceleration pedal of our stress response.

In these instances, our bodies fill with stress hormones like cortisol and epinephrine—they get our bodies moving but trigger health-related issues when remaining elevated over time. Instead of allowing this small chunk of our gray matter to overtake our minds and have these stress hormones decimate our wellbeing, we need to become aware of ourselves. We need to attune to the quieter, subtle vibrations inside that alert us to how we are psychologically feeling, why we are doing what we are doing, and what we need in order to maintain balance.

Turning within, we are more easily able to become aware of a truer state of being.

I am going to offer several meditations over the course of this book to aid you in reconnecting inside—and there are numerous ways to engage with these practices. You are welcome to read along, sentence by sentence, and let the words float within your mind. Conversely, you could read the whole section through and then set the text aside, following the instructions as best as you remember them. Other options include having friends read the meditations out loud to you, recording yourself reading them and playing them back, or downloading the free audio files of me leading these practices from ecstaticself.com/meditations.

Please engage in whatever ways make most sense for you to absorb these meditations to their fullest.

MEDITATION I

First, begin by removing any distractions. Turn off your phone, shut the door, feed the dog. These next few minutes are for you to connect with your deeper self, so give yourself permission to allow these other things to fade to the background. Those text messages will still be there, I promise—let go of your fear of missing out.

Find a way of sitting or relaxing that is comfortable and something you can maintain for ten minutes. You're probably familiar with seeing meditators sitting on the floor, often in a cross-legged position, but that's not necessary if it's not comfortable to you. Relax on a couch or chair—or even lay down—do anything that allows your body to find ease. Find a posture that will allow you to turn your consciousness from the outer world toward the inner.

I am going to guide you through a meditation to connect with your breath. When you are ready, close your eyes and turn your focus inward. How are you feeling? How are you in general? What is your breath like at this very moment? Observe without judgment.

The breath is the gateway to life. Organisms can survive weeks without food, days without water, but only moments without air. Opening to our breath is the way we survive and thrive. Open to oxygen—open to life.

Notice the way in which you are breathing right now. Does your breath come quickly or slowly? Does the inhale or the exhale feel longer or more intense? Do you feel your breath in your collarbones, your torso and ribs, or in your belly? Notice how and where you breathe, and do not judge it. Just let it be as it is.

Have you ever watched a baby or an animal breathe? They both take huge, deep belly breaths. When we were young, we all breathed this way. Then, as we grew up, we started listening to a culture that said, "having a thin waist is attractive." We started sucking-in our abdomens—conforming to beauty standards. Please invite your body to function in the way that it's meant to. Feel your stomach expand on the inhale, contract on the exhale. Maybe even say to yourself, "Soften my belly—soften my belly."

As you feel yourself loosen and experience more freedom, continue to stay curious with what it feels like to simply breathe. The coordination of the countless muscle fibers in the diaphragm, ribs, back and chest in order to make respiration possible is staggering. Think of the millions of little alveoli that have to take in oxygen and release the carbon dioxide molecules. Notice how amazingly complex and beautiful the simple act of breathing is. It is something you do in each moment of every single day—awake, asleep, in sickness, in wellness. You are always breathing. How magnificent it is that your body can do this without your active direction.

Feel the breath fill you. Notice where you feel the sensation of breathing in your body. Maybe you feel it in your throat, maybe in your lungs. Perhaps your life force seems to expand past the physical organs of respiration. Maybe you feel the breath in your shoulders or hips. Maybe you feel it in the space around you, in the open space beyond your shoulders or behind your heart.

Meditative traditions have different words to describe the energy that comes with the breath. Those from India might call it *prana* or *vayu*—from China, maybe *chi*. It is both the physical breath and also something greater. Feel how this life force that you take in and breathe out is not confined by your physical structure. You can feel it in your toes, your hair follicles, in the space around you. Allow yourself to expand to encompass more than just the physical space that your body occupies. Allow your respiratory life force to swim around you, expand and contract, vibrate.

All of life is tidal. Day progresses to night, winter to spring, waves ascend and retreat from the sandy banks of the shore. Everything is cyclical. Our breath is our most immediate connection to the recurrent rhythms of nature. What comes in must go out—what flies up must eventually land. Allow yourself to connect to that rhythm of life and settle into the notion that you are riding your breath. A cosmic traveler riding the waves of life.

Be at one with your essence. Stay here for as long as you would like.

"Breathing dreams like air."
— **F. Scott Fitzgerald, author and essayist**

The practice of turning inward to explore one's inner landscape has been ongoing through much of history. Though relatively new to many Westerners, Eastern civilizations seem to have been exploring mindfulness practices for millennia. Excavations in Mohenjo-Daro and Harappa, two civilizations that reached their peak well before 2500 BCE in current-day Pakistan, have revealed extensive public works like running water and indoor plumbing in most homes—as well as jewelry showing human figures in meditative postures.

Almost every major faith tradition of the world encourages meditative disciplines in at least one of their branches. From Kabbalah in Judaism, to Vedanta and Shivaism in Sanatana Dharma (Hinduism), to the Desert Fathers or Gnostic traditions of Christianity, knowing one's self has been tied to knowing the cosmic source of all.

My own path has guided me through different meditation schools, spiritual traditions, and mindfulness programs. Shortly after I graduated college, I moved into an ashram to commit myself fully to exploring my inner world. My daily routine would begin at five-thirty, when I would stumble out of bed, shower, and tumble into the meditation hall. I would sit there for two hours, fighting off sleepiness, before heading upstairs to prepare breakfast for the other residents and perform my assigned chores for the morning. In the afternoons, I would go on auditions, take acting classes, shoot film projects, and teach yoga. If I wasn't performing at a theatre that night, I would head back to the ashram for evening meditation classes. If I was, I would meditate once I got home, often getting to bed at two or three in the morning.

This was my life for seven years. If I had to travel for work, I would still get up at five a.m. to meditate on the floor of the hotel room. In hindsight, this meditation tradition was too strict and austere for me—they were adamant that the pursuit of internal understanding could happen only within the context of extraordinary measures. I didn't need to go to such an extent to connect with my inner world—it is possible to know your spirit by making deliberate, dedicated efforts within the context of a regular life. I didn't need to become a zealot in order to uncover my truth.

In fact, I now realize that a significant reason I chose such a restrictive life was that I wanted to be exempt from the messy reality of living. I didn't have to work a traditional job, maintain friendships with non-sangha (people outside of the ashram), or dive into existential questions about the meaning of humanness. I wanted to feel pure, aloof, and exempt from the muck of the real world. I was in a perpetual state of sleep deprivation, and there weren't enough fully-awake brain cells to ponder why I was doing this to myself.

Moreover, this tradition allowed me to ignore my sexual identity. The ashram tended toward monasticism—by encouraging celibacy, I was allowed to forgo exploring my orientation. The demanding routines and physical separation from non-spiritual-seekers meant that I couldn't stay out all night dancing at a club or cozy up with a loved one over a bottle of wine. I had to maintain strict discipline. I couldn't see that what I really needed was to let go and relax into being as I was—I shouldn't have tried so hard to seek some form of spiritual perfectionism.

After I left that community, I reconnected with my human side and rediscovered the innate spiritual understanding of my youth. I learned to find ease in my practices of self-study and trust my instincts. I allowed meditation to become something holistic, intuitive, and magical. I learned that self-exploration doesn't solely exist within dogma, doesn't abide by rigid practices. Meditation is a gentle caress between the mind and the soul—it invites us into transient states of awareness that unfurl richer understandings of ourselves.

I went on to explore other paths, schools, and teachers of the spiritual arts and began to see that each of us are enough as we are. We already have inborn tools that we can utilize—we can trust our innate insights. I've visited healing centers in Mysore, temples in Pune, retreats in Hawaii, palaces of worship in Budapest, and sanctuaries in California—all of them encouraging me to listen to my inner guides. Our souls know the way back to our selves; we just have to trust them to lead us.

If you want to know who you really are, meditation can be an immensely powerful tool—a proverbial key for rusty locks. Mediation unlatches doors that have been sealed-up for far too long. Self-awareness is cultivated from time alone—time with yourself. It's simple to undertake and requires no extraordinary devices, circumstances, or efforts. All you have to do is disconnect from your devices and reconnect with your self by riding the breath. Psyche—breath—soul...all are one.

Living in the ashram, there was a quietly whispered belief that meditation could cure all sorts of emotional and mental imbalances. If depression or anxiety were manifesting—you were instructed to meditate more. If you wanted something to happen in your life—meditate more for that, too. While I do acknowledge that mindfulness is a wonderful *part* of a holistic wellness practice—it is not a panacea. It is not, in and of itself, enough to repair decades of harm and emotional trauma. I've seen too many people suffer and hurt themselves further by avoiding proper medical and psychological help. I've seen people avoid speaking out about great wrongs because they trust a greater power to take care of things.

Meditation is not a replacement for active living. Yes, we need to take time to turn within—and we also need to continue having a robust life engaged with a variety of people and environments. To thrive, we require strong social bonds of friendship and love to support us. We need confidants, romantic partners, therapists, workout buddies. We need to go on trips, undertake adventures, explore new paths. Meditation does not replace wild, chaotic living—it should supplement it. It does not replace nights at the movies, spring picnics in bare feet, or salsa dancing lessons. It does not replace group therapy, working a twelve-step program, or seeking medical guidance. Take care of yourself by living your life fully and seek additional support when required.

Until the late twentieth century, neuroscientists believed that neuroplasticity (the ability for the brain to reorganize itself and create new connections) just wasn't possible. They thought that people had a relatively short window to develop a well-structured brain— childhood into adolescence—and then, that was it. A person was set. The rest of their life was just a slow descent downhill, where the gray matter slowly disintegrated to mush.

Fortunately, we now know this isn't the case. Study after study and the advent of functional MRIs have proven that the human brain can recover from injury, disease, and trauma. Scans of meditators and Buddhist monks have shown that the brain can, in fact, change density, shape, and size within as little as eight weeks.[4] Individuals who regularly participate in contemplative exercises show an enhanced ability to recognize patterns that normal brains regularly miss, reconfigure damaged sections within the brain, and reduce areas that trigger pain and reactive responses.[5] Scans have shown that the brains of mindfulness practitioners in their forties and fifties look more like the brains of people in their early twenties.[6] Meditators are able to notice often-missed microexpressions that happen during communication, more keenly observe emotional responses in themselves and others, and are able to mitigate the effects of traumatic experiences—the U.S. Military now teaches it to reduce or eliminate Post-Traumatic Stress Disorder in combat troops.[7]

If we are going to cultivate the neural pathways required to reorganize our relationship with ourselves, it is important that we learn to focus, quiet our surface-level thoughts, and engage in deep awareness. Time spent daily in mindful contemplation can offer just that.

My goal is to offer you a sampling of meditation practices to help you on your journey. Some people will benefit from breathwork, others visualization—some may appreciate active non-doership, mantras, or energetic cultivation. There are as many different styles of mindfulness as there are people to explore them. Find what resonates with you and use that. There is really no right or wrong way to go about cultivating self-inquiry.

You are absolutely welcome to explore all of the meditations I offer throughout the book, going through them sequentially—or you could cherry-pick the ones you'd like, skipping around. Regardless, I would recommend setting aside time each day to go through at least one of the practices. It's almost impossible to start breaking down the compulsory behaviors that keep us separated from our best selves without dedicating regular time to contemplation.

MEDITATION II

Close your eyes and feel the steady fall and rise of your breath. Notice how it feels to sit or lay exactly where you are. Notice the heaviness of your arms, the way your hips press into the surface beneath you. Notice if you feel your abdomen moving at all. Does it expand on the inhale and contract on the exhale?

Whatever is going on for you in the outside world—try to let it go. Trust that those text messages, those deadlines, those conversations can all wait. These few minutes are for you. Just you. Forgive yourself for letting all other obligations go. They'll still be there when you return to your normal life. Take back the mental real estate that they have taken up. They get no more free rent in your mind for the next few minutes.

I want you to imagine what would happen if you let go of all striving. If you stopped trying to achieve, to claim, to become. What if, instead, you simply allowed yourself to be as you are at this moment? How would you feel? Does it scare you to imagine what it would be like if you never attained your goals, developed that body, achieved those accolades? What emotions arise?

Instead of diving back into your usual "doership"—striving, acting, making things happen—what if you simply allow yourself to be who you are? What if you accept that by being whoever you are, it will, by necessity, be the best version of you? By becoming unapologetically ourselves, we conversely achieve our potential. By not doing, we attain everything. By stopping all the pushing and pulling, we gain everything. By being, we become whole.

What would it be like to be radically authentic? What would it feel like to be truly yourself? Maybe you don't know what that would look like, or how it would feel—but your mind knows how to guide you. Your intuition will lead you to that place of wholeness. You don't need to know the precise destination to step in the correct direction. Trust that your inner guidance system will protect and steer you well. Invite yourself to relax into your greatest state of being. Give up the fight for perfection. Choose humanity instead of glamour. Become yourself. Let go of who you "need" to be—and just be you.

Take a few deep breaths and sit with this state that you are cultivating. Be at home with yourself. You are enough. There's no one else you need to be. You can only be you. See how it feels to sit here in the quiet, observing yourself—and noticing what you feel.

> "Through meditation, the higher self is experienced."
> — *The Bhagavad Gita,* **Indian spiritual text**

As we go about our day, our minds provide a running commentary on what is happening around us. But have you ever had a moment where you realized, "The very fact that I can watch myself think means that I must be something deeper than my thoughts?" There are different layers of the mind—and the more superficial stream of consciousness that ebbs and flows is not who we really are. We are something much deeper.

While I provide several guided meditations throughout this book, you don't necessarily need someone to walk you into a state of mindfulness. It is a skill that we can access ourselves at any time, in any circumstances. One of the most valuable tools for becoming more self-aware is being focused. Most people cannot concentrate very well—a study performed by the British Broadcasting Channel found that the average person can only hold an uninterrupted thought in their head for eight seconds—down from twelve seconds a decade prior.[8] The average person is exposed to anywhere from ten-thousand to forty-thousand pieces of advertising over the course of a single day—and it can take nearly twenty-five minutes for a person to return to a task once they've become distracted.[9]

To learn how to focus, it is best to begin with something external. I recommend finding a beeswax candle or a beautiful flower and setting it in front of you, in a place where you can sit or rest easily. A picture of someone you love can also work—whatever object you choose, it should be something that inspires a positive emotion within.

Once you settle into a meditation posture of your choosing, feel your face and body relax. Stare softly at the item before you. Study its nuances. Observe all the tiny details. Find the object fascinating, captivating. How did it grow or come to be this way? If the candle is burning—notice the chemical process that is ongoing to make fire. Can you smell anything? If you touch the object (gently and safely, especially if there are thorns or open flame), how does it feel? Does it make any noise as you interact with it? Could you even taste it?

Come to know this object intimately through all of your senses. Be present to it—let it reveal its mysteries to you. Keep your eyes halfway closed. You don't want to stare too hard—allow the world to become blurry.

The practice of sitting and observing an external object with one-pointed focus is a many-millennia-old tradition. Practiced over time, it will enable you to be less distracted and more aware of what is most important at the moment. I would encourage you to practice this type of meditation for at least a few minutes—for however long feels right to you. The Sanskrit word for this is *dharana*—which means "focus" and "steadfastness."

Once you become good at maintaining awareness on an external object, you can turn to internal loci. Different meditation traditions suggest different focal points—but for the point of our working together, we are going to focus on the heart. Notice the space where you feel the sensation of love upon seeing an old friend for the first time in a long while. When you think of a person dear to you, perhaps a family member or a romantic partner, to what part of your body would you point to represent the seat of your emotions?

Chances are good that your mind has turned to the center of your chest. Some traditions call this area the heart center or the *anahatha chakra*. The ancient Egyptians embalmed this organ and held it sacred—they meanwhile liquified the brain and drained it out of a nostril. Many cultures view the heart-region as the seat of compassion, love, connection, and the nexus point of identity. Though our brains do have heavy processing power, many important emotions like hope, wonder, amazement, love, vulnerability, pain, longing, fear, shame, and belonging emanate from the center of the chest.

When someone betrays your trust, do you call the ensuing sensations brain-ache? No, we refer to it as heartache. When you find yourself sitting around a campfire with childhood friends, roasting marshmallows, where do you experience that feeling of satisfaction? The heart, right? We can think with our heads—we can think with our guts—but we can also process with our hearts.

Using the same meditation technique we used for focusing on a flower, candle, or picture—you can direct your awareness to the space in the middle of your chest. You can imagine a swirling pinprick of energy or a glowing ball of light—you could forgo visualizing and just absorb the sensations. Regardless, the practice is the same: turning our focus within.

This internal gazing cultivates a deeper connection with internal nexus points. Different healing modalities—ranging from acupuncture in Chinese Medicine to *marma* therapy in Ayurveda—describe subtle channels of life-force flowing through our bodies that connect at energetic hubs called *chakras*. The most prominent of which is the heart. By drawing our awareness here, we will cultivate a deeper understanding of ourselves and our spiritual natures.

> *"Nowhere can man find a quieter or more untroubled retreat than in his own soul."*
> — **Marcus Aurelius, Roman Emperor and philosopher**

The experience of heart contemplation unfolds differently for each person. Some report feelings of electricity or lightning—others see colors, shapes, or designs. Many don't experience anything unusual at all—they simply become acutely aware of the expansion and deflation of their ribs. Whatever you observe happening is perfectly alright. Even if it is a feeling of pain or sorrow, that is okay.

When a person turns within, sometimes many years-worth of holding, controlling, and self-denial assert themselves. There will be times that self-exploration releases sorrow, anger, and pent-up rage. Allow yourself to be wherever you are without judgment. Acceptance of our current condition is one of the best skills we can cultivate for meditation and for life. Wherever you are right now is alright—you're exactly where you need to be.

MEDITATION III

Take a deep breath—and let it go. Let go of your connection to the now and enter a state of being that is not constrained by past and future. Enter an awareness that is of timeless resonance. Feel all previous iterations of you and all future possibilities combining to create one, unbound you. All of your personal past is connected with you—everything that has ever happened. Everything that you will eventually do—that exists within you now. Find a state of timelessness.

In this space where all versions of you exist, silently ask that whatever is holding you back from your truest self to thaw and melt away.

Any blocks that you've accumulated, anything sealing you off from your highest potential and your most vibrant self—invite them to dissolve. If you notice any points in your personal history that are causing you pain, keep breathing, and invite them to evaporate.

We all have scars. We all have places where we are tight, knotted, protected. In this moment—invite them all to thaw. You don't need them anymore. What you need most, now, is to connect deeply with your innermost awareness. To enter a flowing, moving state of pure awareness.

Repeat this phrase several times:

"May the parts of me that are frozen—thaw. May the areas where I am holding back—release. May I surrender anything and everything that is keeping me from my best self."

As you repeat these words, feel your crystallized bits liquefying. Feel your life force moving, swelling, swirling. We are fluid, pliable beings—when we become stagnant, that's when problems arise. Release your rigidity and surrender to the fullness of you. Feel fluid freedom moving inside of you.

Keep repeating this invitation for melting. Find a state of letting go. Find a state of grace. Connect with your innermost self. Let this travel into your marrow.

Where does identity exist? Can you point to a definable part of your anatomy that is unequivocally "you?" Your big toe? How about your elbow? If you were to lose a part of your body to amputation, would you be any less "you?"

This existential question has been asked for a very long time—it is one of the tenant practices of the Vedantic meditation tradition, and it is a question very much worth pondering. In today's society, we conflate a person's body, thoughts, and perceptions with their integral essence. But, when we get down to it, can any attribute accurately describe our totality? If we are not the thoughts arising in our minds, if we are not the bodies that carry us around day after day—then, who are we, really?

By turning our focus inside, we will come to better know ourselves beyond the trappings of everyday life. When we question who we are without our fancy clothes, cars, or partners—we reveal a rich and mysterious landscape. There are no easy or solid answers—instead, there is a continual process of exploration. We are voyagers in the landscape of the soul—a terrain that is ever changing and evolving as we grow into and through ourselves.

This is why it is important we develop a sense of curiosity—both about ourselves and the world. When we study something with child-like eyes, we see deeper. Experiences become richer; time slows down. Possessing a hunger to know more, to understand how this particular iteration is different, can be a key to unlocking both self-understanding and a meaning-filled life.

> *"Only through our connectedness to others can we really know and enhance the self. And only through working on the self can we begin to enhance our connectedness to others."*
> — **Harriet Goldhor Lerner, clinical psychologist**

By turning within, we will undoubtedly come to think of our relationships with other people. From the point of pure biology, we are constantly inhaling and exhaling air—and so are all the living creatures around us. We are sharing the same molecules—the atoms that were once part of your body are now being inhaled by a neighbor and will soon be integrated into their physical form.

The water we drink travels into us, mingles with our cells, and passes out into the rivers and waterways—where it will briefly become part of a fish. We hold nothing—everything is on loan to us—and we are in a constant molecular exchange with our fellow cohabitants of Earth. We are part of each other in an incredibly intimate way.

We are all only momentary holders of the quarks, atoms, and quantum bits that make up our bodies. Studies have shown that even the slowest to reproduce parts of our body—our bones—are entirely destroyed and made anew again every seven years.[10] You are literally a new person within the span of seven years, and your cells are made up of the discarded bits of the life forms around you. The food you eat was once the body of a plant or animal who bathed in sunshine, drank from rainstorms, and huddled under lightning.

Not to get too heady, but it's staggering once you consider this. Most of us—especially in America—have such strong personal boundaries of "me" and "mine." But, when we get down to it, we share everything. As we continue on this search for cultivating our fullest identity—we have to be aware of this connection to the life-forms around us.

On a daily basis, we exchange ideas, words, and touch. We further exchange the building blocks of our hearts, arteries, and skin. Studies have shown that people even trade DNA in incredibly intimate experiences—pregnant mothers, for example, can absorb genetic sequences from their unborn children to replace their own.[11] We are all connected in a vast, unknowable marketplace of form and spirit.

From this vantage, it is easy to see the benefit of cultivating compassion for all life-forms. When one part of the organism benefits, so does the whole. We are living in one, interdependent web of life. We can appreciate that each living being is an extension of our very selves: their cells are our cells—their minds are our minds.

This practice of wishing well for all sentient beings is a Buddhist practice called *metta*. You start by wishing well for yourself—*may I be happy*—and then expand that desire to encompass the people you love. From there, you spread it even further to all creatures that live, have lived, or will ever live—*may all beings in creation be happy*. In doing so, we realize the inherent connection between us all—when one benefits, so do all.

Researchers have been studying the results of functional MRI scans of meditators practicing compassion-based *metta* meditation. According to neuroscientist Richard Davidson at the University of Wisconsin—Madison, "Loving-kindness [...] boosts the connections between the brain's circuits for joy and happiness and the prefrontal cortex, a zone critical for guiding behavior."[12] Further studies have shown how gamma waves in the brain increase seven-hundred to eight-hundred percent in meditators when they focus specifically on compassion.[13] These gamma waves are responsible for regulating mood, cognition, attention, working memory and immune function.

With this in mind, let's try to cultivate a sense of empathy, a sense of compassion for each living being around you. By turning your focus to the wellbeing of others, you may just find that you are able to better come home to yourself.

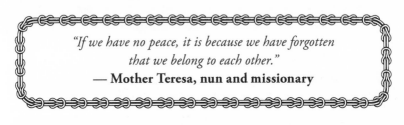

"If we have no peace, it is because we have forgotten that we belong to each other."
— **Mother Teresa, nun and missionary**

MEDITATION IV

Settle into your meditation seat. Close your eyes and breathe. Center yourself into this present moment.

When you are ready, silently wish for yourself to be happy. To be whole. To be contented. Ask for the universe to assist you in coming home to yourself, loving yourself, and finding inner peace.

Sit here, dwelling in this invocation for as long as you need.

Whenever you're ready, bring to mind some individuals who you love. Picture them—imagine them smiling, living their best lives. Wish them well. Wish them every abundance, success, sense of vitality, and happiness. Imagine them thriving—ebullient. Imagine them full of life, laughter, and love. Picture them glowing like the sun just before dusk.

Again, stay here for as long as you would like and need.

From here, become aware of the other living objects in your vicinity. Maybe there's a plant, a flower, a cat. Even stones or water are part of the network of sentient life, according to many traditions. Can you wish them well, too? Can you feel a sense of sacredness, a sense of blessings pervading the world around you?

Can you sense how the wellbeing of one part affects the wellbeing of all? Can you wish everyone and everything happiness for the benefit of all? Can you feel a sense of oneness—and thereby a sense of peace with what is? No matter what apparent drama is going on around you, can you find a sense of blissful stillness—a state of interconnectedness with all life?

As you witness the cosmic intimacy of this meditation—can you hold compassion for each part of the world—yourself included? Sense how each part of this magnificent web of life is just doing its best to endure. Can you bless yourself? Can you feel acceptance for yourself, where you are right here and now—acknowledging that you have your own, specific part to play in this dance of life? Can you allow yourself to just be as you are—realizing your own perfection by simply being part of this larger, interconnected organism?

Can you be as you are right now and see how you are perfect—imperfections and all? Can you hold compassion for yourself, the people you love, and everyone else, too?

One of the greatest tools we can give ourselves for a functional meditation practice is *mantra*. We in the West have been using the word mantra for a long while, now. We talk about mantras being the encouraging affirmations we repeat to ourselves as we walk into the office for a product pitch. The word, however, actually translates to mean "mind protector." They are called such because they give us something to focus on other than the erratic thoughts inside our heads. They give us a brief reprieve.

Another definition of mantra is "stiller of the thought-waves." We enter a calmer, more relaxed state when we repeat mantra. Since this chapter intends to build up your skill set with mindfulness practices that you can apply wherever and however you choose on your self-discovery journey, I would like to share with you a mantra that has been used across cultures. It is connected with the breath—one syllable flows with the inhale and the other with the exhale. Each mantra means something—and that mantra I'm about to impart means "I am that." I am that pure state of awareness beyond thought. I am my essential self.

MEDITATION V

Close your eyes and turn your focus within. Notice the rise and fall of your breath—the rise and fall of your belly. When you are ready, take notice of the sound that your breath makes. Do you hear any repeated noises?

Focus on the inhale. Can you listen for—and silently repeat—the mantra "*soh*?" As you breathe in, try and find the sound *soooooooooo...*

Turn to the exhale. What do you notice? Try and discern the noise "*hum.*" Do you hear the mantra as you breathe out? *Huuuum-mmmmm....*

This mantra repeats every day, with every breath. Each time you breathe, your *prana*—your life force—is calling out, "I am that." I am that pure state of awareness beyond mind, beyond thought. I am pure, vibrant existence.

Sit here, listening for *so'hum* with each breath. *Soh* on the inhale—*hum* on the exhale. Float and rest in and with the breath.

तेजो यत्ते रूपं कल्याणतमं तत्ते पश्यामि योऽसावसौ पुरुषः
सोऽहमस्मि॥१६॥

tejo yat te rūpaṃ kalyāṇatamaṃ tat te paśyāmi yo 'sāv so'hum asmi

"The light which is thy fairest form, I see it. I am that."
— **Issa Upanishad, Vedic text**

Through our meditations together, you have likely experienced a deeper understanding of the definition of "psyche" we discussed earlier—a connection between your breath and the state of your mind. It is no accident that many traditions discuss the link between self-knowledge and how the body respires. To that end, I want to share with you a few, active breathing exercises that can be beneficial for calming the mind and allowing yourself to better focus.

Studies have shown that deep, rhythmic breathing for a few minutes can reduce levels of the stress hormone cortisol by almost 50%.[14] In short bursts, cortisol is great for getting you active and moving—in large doses, however, it increases belly fat, wreaks havoc on the immune system, disrupts sleep, and increases the risk of high blood pressure, high cholesterol, and diabetes.[15] Deep breathing stimulates the vagus nerve, which is an integral part of the parasympathetic nervous system connecting the brain, heart, and gut. Studies are now exploring the possible link between a stimulated vagus nerve and reduced levels of Alzheimer's Disease, migraines, inflammation, and depression.[16] It is beneficial for each of us to take time every day to breathe deeply.

Balancing Breath

As before—sit or lie in a comfortable position. We are going to alternate which nostril we inhale and exhale from. I like to think of this exercise as being similar in shape to an infinity symbol—a sideways number eight. Air flowing from one side to the next and back again.

You're going to need to use one of your hands for this exercise. Bring your hand up to chin-level and turn your palm toward your face. Traditionally, this breathing technique would be executed with the right hand, but please feel free to use whichever side is more comfortable. If you are using your right hand, the thumb will always control the right nostril, and the ring finger will always control the left. Do the opposite if using the other hand.

Using your ring finger, press firmly just above your left nostril, on the side of your nose to block the flow of air. Inhale for about five seconds through the right nostril.

Clamp both sides of your nose by adding in your thumb—and hold your breath for five seconds.

Release the left side of your nose and slowly exhale out of the left nostril for five seconds.

Here's the tricky bit: *keep your thumb over your right nostril.*

Inhale for five seconds through the left side, then close the left side of the nose and hold your breath for five seconds. Release the right nostril and exhale for five seconds.

You have just completed one full round of the balancing breath.

Start off with this breathing pattern of inhaling for five, holding for five, and exhaling for then—a 5:5:5 pattern. You will feel enhanced benefits if you can slow it down further. The next stage would be a 5:10:5 pattern—inhale for five, hold for ten, exhale for five.

Try it again. How does that feel?

Ideally, you'll want to start lengthening the middle section and the exhale out to ten, fifteen, or even twenty seconds. Your breathing patterns might look something like a 5:10:10, 5:15:10, or 5:20:10 arrangement (inhale:hold:exhale).

It can take weeks, months, or years to work up to longer retentions—so stick with what is most comfortable. You should undertake at least ten rounds—but you could undergo this breath pattern for up to eight or nine minutes.

What do you notice about how you feel once you're done? Do you feel more present, more alert? Do you feel a tingling in your skull? Observe any reactions you have and remain curious as to how they change over time.

The name for this breathing pattern is *Anuloma Vilma Pranayama* or, if you are adding the longer pauses, *Nadi Shodana Pranayama*. More simply, Alternate Nostril Breathing.

If you found that breathing exercise useful, I highly recommend exploring the rich tradition of *pranayama*—one of the eight limbs of a yogic practice. I am going to share two more breathing exercises that are good for releasing stress and cooling an agitated mind. When you feel hot, irritated, irritable, or on-edge, these routines can be great ways to bring yourself back into harmony. If you suffer from low blood pressure, asthma, or are currently experiencing a bout of the cold/flu, please skip over them.

The Lunar Breath

In the health-science tradition of Ayurveda, the two nostrils are ascribed attributes that can affect our mood, health, and wellbeing. The right side is considered hot, solar, and active. The left side is considered cooling, lunar, and restorative. Most of us live in an agitated world: everything moves fast, burns bright, and is stimulating. Nearly all humans alive today need to learn to slow down, enjoy the moment, and relax a bit more. Connecting with this quieter side can be very helpful as we move about an ever-faster, ever-hotter world.

Find a comfortable position, ideally seated with an erect spine, and cover the right side of your nose with your right thumb. Inhale fully—for about five seconds—and then clamp off your nose and hold the breath. You can follow the same patterns suggested above (5:5:5, 5:10:5, etc.). Keep the ring finger covering the left side and exhale fully on the right. Then, repeat on the *same side*—do not alternate like we did above.

By inhaling exclusively on the left and exhaling on the right, we stimulate the left side of our nasal cavity, bringing in more of that cooling, lunar energy to calm us and allow the rippling waters of the mind to still. You can breathe in this manner for as long as feels useful—at least twelve repetitions. The traditional name for this exercise is *Chandra Bhedana Pranayam*.

Tubular Breathing

Stick out your tongue and roll it into a tube (if you cannot, do not worry—the ability to do this is genetically determined, and I will provide you with another option momentarily). Inhale through your mouth as if you were sucking in air from a straw. Close your lips, retain the breath for however long feels comfortable, and then exhale slowly through the nose. Repeat as many times as feels comfortable—inhaling through the hollow space created by your tongue and exhaling out of the nostrils. This is called *Sheetali Pranayam*.

If you find it impossible or uncomfortable to roll your tongue, you can explore a similar exercise. For this variation, pull your cheeks wide as if you were grimacing and inhale through loosely clenched teeth. Continue as described above—retain the breath and exhale out of the nose. This exercise is named *Sheetkari Pranayam*.

Regardless of which version of this breath pattern you are exploring, pay attention to the coolness of the air entering your body. Examine the physical sensations on your tongue, against your gums, around your teeth. Be alert and curious as to how your body and mind respond to these exercises.

> *"Best be still; best be empty.*
> *In stillness and emptiness we find where to abide.*
> *Talking and moving we lose the place."*
> — **Lao Tzu, author of the *Tao Te Ching***

I enthusiastically encourage you to begin a daily practice of mindfulness—sitting in silence first thing each morning or last thing before bed. Taking time daily to turn within will be beneficial for reconnecting with that essential self. Sit for however long feels right for you—it is best not to push or force this endeavor. Let it evolve over time in whatever ways feel best.

A general rule of thumb is to work up to sitting for however many minutes that you are years old. For example, a thirty-year-old person should eventually strive to meditate for thirty minutes a day.

An eighty-five-year-old: eighty-five minutes. Obviously, this will take time—be kind to yourself. Do not rush—do no harm. Let meditation unfold naturally.

Time spent in self-inquiry should be something to which you look forward, something that makes you feel better than if you'd skipped it. Try to strike the right balance between developing discipline and being relaxed. It can be beneficial to set up a space that exists solely for the purpose of self-exploration. Create a sacred spot with some flowers, a candle, soothing music—fashion a retreat in your home to which you will long to return. Put up some decorative artwork that calms your mind, toss down cushy pillows that make you sigh with contentment.

I recommend giving yourself a sixty-eight-day challenge of trying to meditate every day. I suggest that number because it takes sixty-eight repetitions for a new neural pathway to grow.[17] In that time, meditation will become a habit and something that you will more easily slip into experiencing. If sixty-eight days seems too intimidating, maybe begin with just a week. Find whatever calls to your spirit.

Over time, mindfulness will help you become much more self-aware and self-connected. It is difficult to know the self we want to root into if we are constantly having our awareness pulled outside. We have to become conscious of—and delve into—our depths. We need to know our essences.

Ultimately, we are the only traveling companions we have through life. We need to know ourselves intimately in order to make the most of our journey. We need to find quiet in order to reconnect with our truths—we need to turn within.

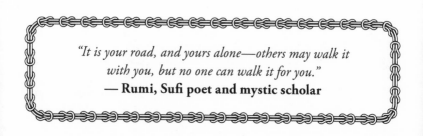

"It is your road, and yours alone—others may walk it with you, but no one can walk it for you."
— **Rumi, Sufi poet and mystic scholar**

EXERCISE

Write out your meditation plan. How/when/for how long are you going to sit? Give yourself a guide to follow—and watch how you evolve over time.

I will strive to sit for _____ minutes each day at roughly _____ am/pm. I will keep this practice going for a minimum of _____ days.

SUMMARY:

— Connect with your breath; it is the greatest indicator of the state of your spirit.

— Begin the practice of turning within to know yourself. There are many ways and means to explore a mindfulness journey—so use what calls you.

— Set aside time every day for silence and to inquire inside.

Chapter 3:

STEEPENING CURVES

*"It is our birthright to uncover the soul—to remove the layers
of fear or shame or apathy or cynicism that conceal it."*
**— Elizabeth Lesser, writer and founder
of the Omega Institute**

We just spent a chapter diving into our subconscious selves. Who are we, really, beneath the mental chatter? What is it that we are trying to connect with—that deeper identity from which we feel disconnected? What causes our sense of lack or inauthenticity?

We approached these questions from a meditative level and tried to avoid qualitative thought. Now, we are going to do the opposite—in this chapter, we are going to utilize imagination and cognitive reasoning to discern more about our innate self.

Grab your pen again. It's time to dream up the ten best descriptive words of who you believe yourself to be at your essence. The words don't need to be literal—if you want to call yourself "turquoise," go for it. Think of this as a brainstorming session—there are no right or wrong answers. The important thing is to pull verbiage that feels authentic to you.

The best words to describe who I really am at my core:

- _____
- _____
- _____
- _____
- _____

- _____
- _____
- _____
- _____
- _____

Take a look at what you wrote and what commonalities do you notice? Are there any trends?

General observations:

_____
_____
_____
_____
_____
_____
_____
_____
_____
_____

Circle your favorite three items from the list—we are going to do some mind-mapping with them. Put the three words in the middle of each of the circles below. At the terminus of each spoke leading away from them, add a related word that feels equally true to you. So, for example, if one of my central words were "creative," some of the words I would add to the surrounding lines might be: artistic, unique, vibrant, playful, unexpected, challenging, or norm-breaking.

Take your time with this—there is no rush. Make sure every word you choose feels authentic to you. You can always cross-out or erase a word that you didn't end up liking.

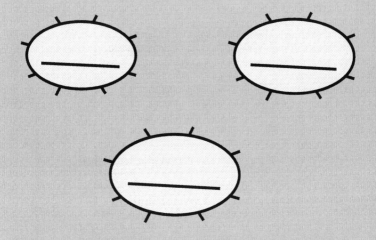

Take a gander at all the new words you penned and circle ones that mean the most to you. We are going to come back to them in a little bit.

Let's create another list. For this one, please generate ten words that you know are definitely *not* you. What are some descriptors that feel inauthentic to your essence? What are words that rub you the wrong way or make you feel unsettled? Sometimes, by revealing what we are not, we can better see what we really are.

Descriptors that feel incongruous to me and how I live my life:

- _____
- _____
- _____
- _____
- _____

- _____
- _____
- _____
- _____
- _____

Notice if there any items on this list that inspire a gut-level response in you. When you read them, do you experience any sort of emotional jump or clenching? These words might reflect what is called your "shadow side," which is a topic we will devote the entire next chapter to exploring. Bookmark those words for now by circling them with your pen.

On to a third list. These are words that inspire or excite you in some way—perhaps they are qualities that you aspire toward. Explore vocabulary about the person you've always wanted to be. They might not feel entirely authentic to you as you are right now, but they can be guideposts demarcating where you might be headed.

Words that I want to become, own, or develop into being:

- _____
- _____
- _____
- _____
- _____

- _____
- _____
- _____
- _____
- _____

Circle your top three—and then repeat the brain mapping exercise we used above. Explore how your top words can branch out into other descriptors. You may uncover new language around the person you wish to grow into being.

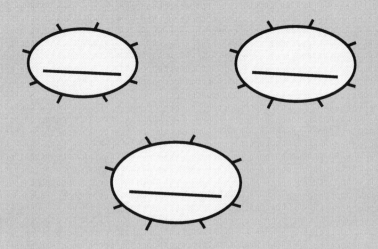

Circle any words that jump out at you from this mind-mapping exercise.

For our final step, look back over the words that have made the biggest impressions on you in this exercise—from any of the lists. They won't be hard to find—pay particular attention to the words you circled along the way. It doesn't matter if they would be considered either positive or negative—retrieve and collate them in the space provided below.

The words that jump out at me most strongly are:

- _____   - _____
- _____   - _____
- _____   - _____
- _____   - _____
- _____   - _____

Sit in silence for a few moments, letting this final list of words marinate inside of you. Whatever you are feeling, try not to be critical of your impressions. Let go of any notion of right or wrong, good or bad. Let your experience of your key words be whatever it is. After you've had some time to listen, observe, and reflect—journal on your takeaways from seeing this list brought together.

Observations on the distilled list:

_____
_____
_____
_____
_____
_____
_____
_____
_____
_____

> *"Beautiful young people are accidents of nature,*
> *but beautiful old people are works of art."*
> **— Eleanor Roosevelt, First Lady**

The famous drag queen and business mogul, RuPaul Charles, has a catchphrase: "We're all born naked, and the rest is drag." As he explains, we arrive in this world without any external trappings, without a formed expression of identity. Then, for the rest of our lives, we try on different costumes, experiment with different personas—examining how we fit each—until we cultivate an exterior that we label as being "us." Some people, drag queens included, are aware that their external facades are pure fabrication—just glitter, tulle, and makeup. Other people believe their identities to be real—that they genuinely are the stockbrokers or dog walkers they pretend at being. They think of themselves as really being house-husbands or lady executives, dentists or dietitians.

The truth is that there's an element of putting on a proverbial costume for every one of us. We have to come to terms with the notion that each of us is performing a persona—and, since life is one big game of dress-up, we can choose to discard the pieces that are no longer fitting and replace them with better accoutrements from the shelf.

EXERCISE

We spent time exploring words that might describe our personal truths. Now, let's do the opposite. Create a list of qualities that feel antithetical to your essence—but are still part of how you perform in the world. What are some qualities that you consciously know are not intrinsically aligned with you but are part of how you present to the world? What are elements that feel costume-y, fake, or incongruent to your true self? Try to get specific about behaviors, actions, or patterns that might have at one time served you, but do so no longer. This time, when you identify a word, write out a sentence to explain why.

Inauthentic parts of my life (and a reason why they're feeling so) include:

_____because_____

_____because_____

_____because_____

_____because_____

_____because_____

_____because_____

_____because_____

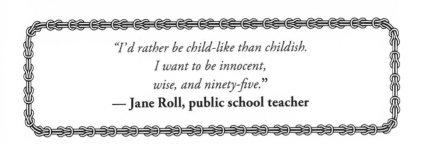

Deep down, all living creatures want the same thing. We want to feel loved and free to share that love with another. We desire respect, a sense of being valued and appreciated. We long to see another person in their entirety and have them see us themselves. We crave acceptance and meaningful connections with others. Or, as Sarah Hodgson (dog trainer extraordinaire) says, "We all just want to feel safe, understood, and valued"—both humans and animals alike.

As young spirits entering the world, we are intrinsically connected to these desires. We long to be held, touched, coddled, doted upon, seen. We are enthusiastically ourselves—rooted into our truth as loving, kind, compassionate, generous souls. As we grow older, however, we pull away from those basic longings and qualities to guard ourselves—we erect inauthenticity as a form of protection.

We learn to anticipate pain, to be wary of others, to fear the wider world. We come to expect disappointment. Instead of giving love freely, we miserly guard it except for in the most extraordinary of circumstances. We lie about ourselves and cheat people of our humanity—choosing protection and control over vulnerability and connection.

This is normal—but it is not healthy. We need to consciously dismantle the guards we have constructed to keep us safe. If you reflect on younger versions of yourself, you will see a person who is wide-eyed and fully exposed to the world. But they exist in a society that demands that they conform to expectations and conventions. They are growing up within families that ask them to merge with the tribe's identity. They go to schools where peer pressure crushes their uniqueness.

All too quickly, that glittering individuality gets covered over. You disconnect from yourself to survive the gauntlet that is adolescence. You sculpt and define a persona of increasing complexity that shields your vulnerable self from the world—and then, after fully armoring-up, realize the fort that you'd constructed to keep others out is a prison locking up your true self within. The rest of life is subsequently spent battling through the armaments and ramparts to uncover the treasure buried within.

We have to undo the trappings of "who I should be" and "what people expect me to do" in order to access our potential. We have to question why we crave safety over freedom, security over wild unknowing. As scary as it is to surrender the behaviors, beliefs, and patterns that have kept us protected since childhood, it's time to acknowledge that most of these tools are no longer serving us well. Just as you wouldn't choose the same games, music, or Lisa Frank Trapper Keeper as you did when you were seven years old, you shouldn't be choosing the same protection methods as an adult.

> "When I was a child, I spoke and thought and reasoned as a child. But when I grew up, I put away childish things."
> — **First Corinthians, Christian New Testament**

It is important to recognize that you are much safer now than you were when you were young and in the throes of forming your identity. You are no longer subject to the whims of the grownups in the room—you have agency to exercise your authority. Along with a fully developed brain, you also possess a better sense of what actually endangers your wellbeing, what situations should encourage caution, and who to (and not to) trust.

As adults, we come to understand that personal essence is strangled by overly robust barriers. This is not the same as personal boundaries—those are important and will become stronger as we come to know ourselves more intimately. No, we realize that hiding our truest self leads to dissatisfaction with life and general malaise. It may take a sledgehammer or a wrecking ball, but those walls must come down. If you want to have meaningful connections with both others and yourself, you need to deconstruct the battlements that are keeping your inner light at bay.

> *"We hold on till our hands bleed. And in that self-shattering persistence, we fail to see the answer: Just let go."*
> — **Yasmin Mogahed, Muslim scholar**

Perhaps someone in your family struggled with addiction, perhaps you felt abandoned by your caretakers, maybe you grew up in an environment where you could not fully be your glorious self. Times are now different—you have matured; you have moved on. It's time to examine what unspoken beliefs are holding you back from your best self—and face them head-on.

EXERCISE

Let's break out the crayons again. I want you to create artwork contrasting how you currently feel and compare it with how you imagine feeling when living rooted into your authentic self. Drawing one—life as it is right now. Drawing two—how life would be if you were aligned with your essence.

Drawing One—How You Feel Presently:

Drawing Two—How Your Best Life Feels:

"I must be willing to give up what I am in order to become what I will be."
— **Albert Einstein, atomic scientist and watchmaker**

"The first step toward change is awareness," says psychologist Nathaniel Branden. We reach a point in our development where we recognize that we could be living differently, that we could be making better choices. We might see that, "I'm not living my best life. I am cut off from what makes me, *me*. I am not being genuinely myself, and this is a problem. I want to change; I want to live a radically engaged and integrated life; I want to be authentically myself."

"The second step," Branden continues, "is acceptance." It's not about rushing out to enact the change you desire—it's about learning to accept being where you are. If you view coming home to yourself as being some sort of war, a battle that you have to conquer, you're likely to become mired in the first charge. We need to approach ourselves with gentleness, compassion, and understanding. We need to start by allowing ourselves to be exactly where we are—and gradually make changes from there.

It took decades to erect the barriers that keep us from our truth— we are not going to dismantle them over a weekend. They went up stone by stone, and they will have to come down the same way. Sometimes, we'll pull out one rock, and a huge cascade of others come down with it. Yay for those days—the joy of abrupt progress. Other times, we have to slog with the sledgehammer for what feels like ages and relatively little results. Sometimes, growth may even feel like the stones have gone back up, much to our horror and dismay.

The path toward self-realization is winding—it frequently does not progress in a straight-shot toward the goal. Sometimes we have to re-explore old patterns by circling back to them, trying again what didn't serve us well last time. We may need to examine them from a new angle to be certain that they did not bring us lasting happiness. I perceive self-exploration as a sort of spiral—we may feel like we are returning, but we are actually coming back around at a higher elevation. Even if you feel like you're stuck in the same rut—you are still likely moving forward.

Be compassionate and gentle with yourself—you do not need to be perfect; you do not need to evolve rapidly. It is important to appreciate that everyone's journey is unique; one person's path and timing will not look like another's. By reminding ourselves to not compare our progress, we can better appreciate the perfection in our own way of developing. Let us all have the grace and patience to accept ourselves for being where we are—and to acknowledge that lasting change takes many days to cultivate.

> "It's dark because you are trying too hard.
> Lightly child, lightly. Learn to do everything lightly.
> Yes, feel lightly even though you're feeling deeply.
> Just lightly let things happen and lightly cope with them."
> — **Aldous Huxley, English writer and philosopher**

EXERCISE

What are personal misbeliefs that you know to be untrue but are still shaping your life? Such might include ideas like, "If I let anyone see the real me, they will hurt me," or, "Love is a weakness, not a blessing." Write out some lessons that you now identify as being flat-out lies. Since the first step is acknowledgment, we need to articulate the paradigms that are holding us back.

_____

_____

_____

_____

_____

_____

_____

_____

_____

_____

_____

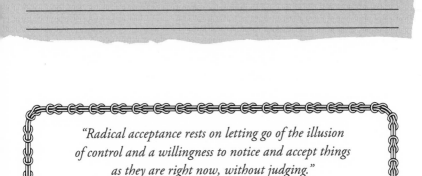

"Radical acceptance rests on letting go of the illusion
of control and a willingness to notice and accept things
as they are right now, without judging."
— **Marsha M. Linehan, American psychologist and author**

Throughout the book, I offer ways to strengthen our connection to ourselves—and it is critical to remember that with whatever I suggest, its polar opposite is often equally valid. For example, when we discuss finding acceptance with ourselves as we are right now, we should consider:

I have complete agency to change my life. I have the ability to choose my actions, cultivate my best self, and manifest my destiny. I am the helmsman of my future.

Simultaneously:

Having control over the flow of my life is an illusion. Invisible forces have guided me to where I am now—I am powerless to fight against their currents. Karma and the claws of fate steer me—and I am helpless to rebel against them.

I may sound befuddled or deranged for asserting both perspectives are in earnest—but so it is. In fact, the ability to hold competitive and sometimes dissonant ideologies—and recognize their respective value—is a sign of good mental health. When we get too caught up in believing that there is only one correct vantage, one absolute truth, that's when we become blinded by righteous zealotry. Instead, if we can hold separate and conflicting ideologies and recognize the merit in each, we will be able to stay much more adaptable in our responses.

If you know something to be true—examine its opposite. There is likely to be equally valid substance there.

This notion of diametrically opposed pairs is fundamental to the laws of the universe: matter and anti-matter, north and south ends of a magnet, Democrats and Republicans, day and night, high tide and low. One is not better than the other—both are needed to achieve balance and homeostasis. I bet there is an inverted anti-matter universe out there with your doppelgänger merrily frolicking through a field and deeply contented with themself (but, as we cannot contact her/him/them and ask for their advice, it's best if we keep the focus on the you of this dimension).

Newton said it best, "Every reaction has an opposite and equal reaction." When one exists, so does its foil. You can have full control over your destiny—and, simultaneously, have zero control over your destiny. Life is a rollercoaster—you are firmly strapped into one of the carts and unable to escape, but you are also the builder of the ride and are laying the tracks with every choice you make. Seem complicated? I thought so.

If we can avoid seeing the world in black and white—and instead opt for shades of gray— then we can start to live in more profound grace and harmony with our surroundings. It's easy to get caught up in the notion that one vantage is more correct than another—but the truth often lies somewhere in between both. As the infamous Facebook relationship status option once offered, "It's complicated."

Work on holding opposing notions as equally plausible. Try to believe that you are both infinitely powerful and responsible for your wellbeing—as well as powerless and lacking personal agency to enact effective change. There is truth somewhere between the two.

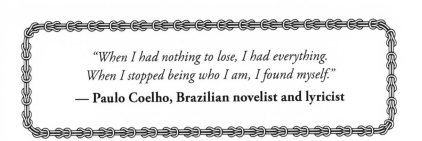

Let's examine these diametrically opposed ideas regarding control. Yes, your thoughts and actions are powerful. Your choices have led you to where you are—and you have the ability to choose differently, moving forward. Only you can initiate the process of reconnecting with your innermost self. You are the person who is ultimately responsible for the way you are. It is up to you to manifest the growth you are looking for—no one else will ever give it to you or do it for you.

Conversely, the opposite can also be argued. The universe is going to bring endless surprises and challenges with which to cope—and you are at their mercy. Face it, each day you wake up, make a plan, and by lunchtime your agenda has often been discarded due to unforeseen complications. Dramas arise, car keys aren't where they are supposed to be, and your best friend called to announce that she and her boyfriend of ten days are eloping to Tijuana. The way things turn out is outside of our power—we are buffered by unknowable forces that push and pull on us. It's amazing that we have ended up where we are today. As the Yiddish proverb goes, "We plan, God laughs."

Can you sense the inherent truth in these two, seemingly opposed sentiments? I have agency to change my life—but I am also powerless. I have been forced to accept both. There have been areas of my life where I have felt incredibly capable of effecting change—I have enacted developments for myself and my surroundings. Contrarily, there have been countless times when, no matter how I strive, nothing works out. I smash my head against impenetrable glass. I study all the self-help books I can lay my hands on; I practice manifestation as if it were my lifeline—but nothing shifts.

> "I know I'm getting older because my Kindle is turning
> into a self-help library. I'm not interested in
> Fifty Shades of Gray. I'm interested in the
> Life-Changing Magic of Tidying Up.
> *Yes, how to de-clutter my home to achieve inner peace*
> *and my optimum level of success. That's what your*
> *30s is all about: How can I turn this shit around?*
> *I'm a terrible person; I'm not happy with where I am.*
> *How can I turn this shit around?!*
> *Help me, Tony Robbins! Help me!!"*
> **—Ali Wong, comedian and screenwriter**

One explanation for the coexistence of these opposing truths is that life is a balance between active choice and pre-established karma.

Karma has become a common term in Western society over the past few decades. Many summarize it as, "What goes around, comes around." While that is mostly true, a more precise explanation would be that karma is the experiences a person needs to undergo in order to return to balance—based on their previous actions.

Every time a person makes an action of some kind, it creates a psychic impression in their energy field—almost like a golf ball denting the side of a tin can. That impression will call to other possible experiences, asking for a mirrored event to bang in from the opposite side and return it to its un-dented state. If you indulged in excess, you will subconsciously call out for scarcity to help you learn balance. If you intentionally hurt someone else, your karma will call for someone else to do similar to you so you can know what if feels like and learn from the experience.

It's not an exact pairing—it's not "an eye for an eye"—but it is about seeing experiences as a teacher that helps us grow. Karma is a learning tool to help us eventually realize that nothing is inherently good or bad—it's just is. Pain and pleasure are opposite sides of the same coin. We see that anything could be deemed positive or negative depending upon our vantage.

Yes, it can be immensely painful to watch someone get hurt, especially when it seems entirely undeserved. I often become nauseated when I see children abused or loved ones battling life-threatening illnesses. Like many of us, I plead with God or howl at the moon in despair—wondering how life could be so unjust.

This feeling of unfairness, however, changes when viewed from an Eastern perspective. In many spiritual traditions, the idea of a soul taking numerous lifetimes to learn its lessons is commonly held. Karma does not necessarily have immediate repercussions—the karma related to an action might manifest thirty years in the future, or even in a subsequent incarnation.

What this means is that each of us has strong karma directing their life—and it causes sudden upheavals that seem to come out of nowhere. That football injury you suffered during sophomore year of high school? It might be the result from a time when you broke a teammate's arm two lifetimes ago. That award that you won but never felt like you deserved? Perhaps you put in the hard work during a previous time around.

Each of us has experiences that we must go through, based on our past behavior—much of which we are not even cognizant of. If you doubt the validity of karma/pre-birth experiences (and I realize that it is still considered a fringe concept in much of Western society), I invite you to spend time around young children. It's quickly clear that they came into this life with strong opinions, proclivities, behavioral patterns, and knowledge about things with which they should be virtually inexperienced.

For many, the only justification for such abilities is past life experiences. Random genetic combinations just don't provide enough evidence to explain how children know what they do and why they have such defined personalities. (Some argue animals are the same—I am fairly certain that my dog was a sort of activist in his last life, the way he continuously protests and enacts sit-ins to demand his terms.)

This is also why traditional psychotherapy—while a tremendously beneficial modality—is somewhat limited in its ability to diagnose the origins of behavioral problems. When the ability to dissect trauma is limited to experiences that a client actively remembers, healing can only reflect back to the earlier parts of this particular incarnation. That doesn't mean that someone can't do incredible house cleaning with a therapist—it just means that some patterns and behaviors may seem unjustified given the happenings of this present lifetime.

> "Life will give you whatever experience is most helpful for the evolution of your consciousness. How do you know this is the experience you need? Because this is the experience you are having at the moment."
> —**Eckhart Tolle, spiritual teacher and writer**

We should strive to hold compassion for ourselves and what's happened to us. We should endeavor to hold a view that the results of our actions are more or less outside of our control. If you find yourself tremendously successful, having built a business empire by your twenty-third birthday valued at six-billion dollars—don't pat yourself on your back too hard. Similarly, if everything you've ever touched has burned to a crisp and fluttered into ashes—don't blame yourself, either. We do the best we can with what we are given. As Pulitzer Prize-winning editorialist Mary Schmich writes, "Whatever you do, don't congratulate yourself too much, or berate yourself either."

This perspective on karma should encourage us to take full responsibility for the choices we are actively making in this lifetime. Each day, at each moment, we are laying the tracks for future events. If you want people to treat you with compassion in the future, offer them empathy and kindness now—even if you think them undeserving. If you want others to be honest and transparent with you—strive for openness and earnestness now.

You get to choose your behavior. You may not get to control the course of events or the unfolding of your life, but you do choose how you respond. You can actively strive toward your best and most radiant self, regardless of what is happening around you. You can opt to live authentically and bravely—even if you presently feel far from your goals.

By actively making changes to our current way of being, we will alter the manifestation of our futures. We can forge new trajectories—and while it may take time to see results, the grooves are being formed. As physicist Newton explained in his second law of physics, "An object in motion tends to stay in motion." Meaning that, once we start moving, we can stay moving—we can alter and add to our momentum. And the more energy you put toward steering yourself in a particular direction, the easier it'll be to keep heading that way.

> *"Life is more a matter of choosing than knowing.*
> *He could never know the eventual destination of his path,*
> *but he could always choose in which direction to take each step."*
> **—Matthew Woodring Stover, novelist**

You don't need to be able to clearly see the destination in order to know the direction you need to head—trust your inner guidance. If you want to walk to Indiana—all you really need to know is which compass point to follow. Don't let indecision hamper you—listen for your inner guide. If you don't adjust your path, you'll end up where you're headed right now—and I guarantee that there are better vistas to be had.

Hopefully, you've taken my suggestion and begun a daily mindfulness practice. I'm going to add two more short tasks onto your daily routine. For the next sixty-eight days, I want you to create two lists. In the morning, write out a list of things for which you are grateful. These can be items that are already present in your life, for which you want to offer thanks—or things that you would be grateful to see manifest in the future. Be specific—and, either way, list them as already having become a part of your world.

In the evening, create a short list reflecting on positive experiences that happened over the course of the day. Get specific about the blessings you observed—cement these memories in place by writing about them.

In the morning, write: I am grateful for

_____.

In the evening, write: Today, this amazing thing happened:

_____.

When you are done writing either session, read aloud what you wrote. Speaking will fire further neurons to rewire your brain and draw the learning deeper.

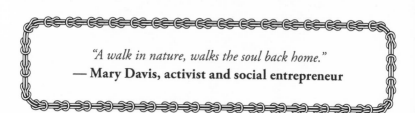

"A walk in nature, walks the soul back home."
— **Mary Davis, activist and social entrepreneur**

In our modern world, it can be challenging to hear the call of our inner voices. Surrounded by car horns, computers, cellphones, and hollering deadlines—it can be difficult to connect to our inner guide. If you are going through these exercises and struggling, it may be helpful to go outside and rediscover nature.

Many of us live in cities or suburbs where starlight is a distant memory, where we strain to remember when our toes last felt dirt. We come from the earth, and we will go back to it. A disconnect from nature often correlates to a disconnect from spirit. I invite you to build a fire, climb a tree, sit by a flowing body of water, or meander over a wooded hillside. You may find yourself there.

We are cyclical beings. Our hearts beat in each moment of the day; our breaths travel in and out; we wake and we rest. We live our lives amidst day and night, spring and autumn, the waxing and waning of the moon. Many of us have abandoned our connection to these natural rhythms for the phosphorescent glow of modern life. In doing so, we have lost the rhythmic flow within. If you find yourself regularly up past midnight or sleeping until noon—it'll be hard to hear your body speaking.

So—power-down your phones, put on some sneakers, and step outside. Reintegrate with the beauty and the majesty that is the natural world, of which you are a part. Feel the precious organism, the breathing ecosystem to which you belong. Step into dewy grass. Watch a roaring fire transform cellular matter into light. Observe the tide and remind yourself how you are part of all of this.

Recent studies have shown benefits to spending a minimum of two-hours surrounded by nature over the course of a week. Psychologist Matthew White says, "It decreases heart rate, decreases blood pressure, decreases stress, cortisol, [and] improves psychological well-being." Additionally, Greg Bratman at the University of Washington has studied individuals with mild depression and has linked improvement with significant time spent in an outdoors environment.[1]

Reconnect with the natural wonders, with the elements, and you will likely kindle a re-coupling with your truer self. Experience your wild heart galloping under a full moon—your identity breaking free of the suit-and-ties of modern living. "By discovering nature, you discover yourself," says Maxime Lagacé, Canadian hockey player.

> "My soul is awakened, my spirit is soaring
> And carried aloft on the wings of the breeze;
> For above and around me the wild wind is roaring,
> Arousing to rapture the earth and the seas."
> — **Anne Brontë, novelist**

EXERCISE

Plan some time outdoors within this coming week. You can even break the requisite two-hour requirement into four, thirty-minute chunks and not lose any of the positive impact. But try to get the full two-hours, if at all possible.

This week, I will take time to explore nature by:

Going to _____ at this date and time: _____
_____

Going to _____ at this date and time: _____
_____

Going to _____ at this date and time: _____
_____

Going to _____ at this date and time: _____
_____

While you're outside, make sure you're not distracted by technology. I recommend bringing a pen and a notebook to jot down any inspiration that strikes you. It's a good time to journal on your current experience of coming into wholeness.

SUMMARY:

— Get clear about who you think you are and who you are not.

— Identify the misbeliefs that are holding you back from your best self.

— Observe and modify the choices you are currently making that are creating your destiny.

— Reconnect with the natural world.

Chapter 4:

ENTERING THE CREVASSE

"One does not become enlightened by imagining figures of light, but by making the darkness conscious."
— **Carl Jung, founder of analytical psychology**

How many of us have feared invisible monsters—an alligator under the bed, a tentacled blob beneath the stairs, a wooly giant in the closet? Not only children, but adults too, can be afraid of what they cannot see. Ominous shadows don't just lurk in the corners of the world—they are also in the corners of our minds. There are parts of ourselves that we avoid shining lights on—but so long as we shun or remain afraid of parts of who we are, we will struggle to come into wholeness.

I am an advocate of opening up to every part of yourself—the good and the bad, the ugly and the pretty. It's important to see each portion of ourselves as sacred, holy, and beautiful. For as long as we relegate aspects of our psyche to the basement, we will never be able to live an integrated life.

Further, there is danger in leaving sections of our mind unexamined. Things fester, mold, and grow wiggling arms when kept in the dark. "Shame derives its power from being unspeakable," says sociologist Brené Brown. What makes our unexamined bits so terrifying is the very fact that we dare not face them head-on. When we feel ashamed—when our hidden desires seem incongruous with our outer personas—that is when emotional crises can arise. If we can, instead, face our buried passions with openness, honesty, and courage, we can open into a healed state.

We have to accept ourselves in our totality. As long as we try to sever parts of our identity, we will be unwell. How can any animal healthily function without one of its legs to run on? How are we supposed to make it through life—proverbially hobbled—when we are cutting ourselves off at the knees? We cannot survive as vivisected persons—we need all of our parts in order to live a vibrant, full life.

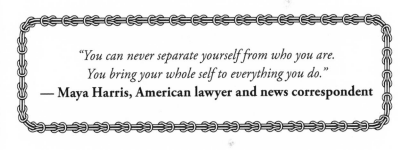

"You can never separate yourself from who you are.
You bring your whole self to everything you do."
— **Maya Harris, American lawyer and news correspondent**

A mentor of mine regularly repeated, "Anything that is repressed will express itself inappropriately." I reflect on the profundity of that statement rather frequently. That which I am afraid of will find some way of creeping out of my subconscious and running amuck. Those shadows frighten me for good reason. By being repressed, they are likely to assert themselves in inappropriate—and sometimes unkind—ways. I keep a steady watch out for telltale signs of buried parts of my psyche rearing their heads. When I witness myself becoming irrational with my emotions, I take notice. A seemingly benign stimulus sets me off? Perhaps, it's because whatever-that-trigger-was is highlighting something within myself that I wish weren't there.

Let me offer an archetypical example that is based on a true story that I heard. Imagine, if you will, a barbershop owner who regularly abandons his customers to bolt outside and yell at trans-identified people walking down the sidewalk, minding their own business. Why should he respond so viscerally and angrily? Perhaps he has past trauma involving trans people, and their presence triggers him. It is a possible explanation for his cruelty—but not likely strong enough to justify the profundity of his angst. More probably, gender-nonconforming people scare him because they highlight an area of himself that he does not wish to acknowledge. He might be frightened that he, too, is in some way non-heteronormative—and that repressed fear expresses itself inappropriately.

Another example I witness fairly often is people openly fat shaming another person for taking up too much space on the subway. Through eye-rolls, unkind facial expressions, and hurtful slurs, people make their overt displeasure known. Most likely, that round-bodied person knows that they are exceeding the limits of their plastic seat—they are aware of the fact that they are overweight. Do the passersby think that they are doing the person a favor by consciously and callously picking on their body size? Why can't the observers just quietly keep their focus on themselves and be polite?

Oftentimes, these actions stem from witnessing traits in another that they fear to be true within themselves. Anything that unduly provokes us—anything that we irrationally hate, avoid, or decry—is likely to be a buried part of our own psyche that we dread. If you are unreasonably negative about someone—and that person is not hurting anyone else, inciting conflict, or inflicting pain—it may suggest that you share some sort of kinship with them.

How often have we seen that the most openly homophobic politicians are closeted themselves? How often do we discover that the most slut-shaming evangelicals secretly keep mistresses and families hidden in their proverbial (or literal) attics? Whatever sparks irrational emotion might be portions of our identities that we've tried to bury. For whatever reason, we consciously or unconsciously deemed a part of ourselves unacceptable and tried to either ignore or sever it.

In the previous chapter, I asked you to create a list of things that you are *not*—keywords that you felt were antithetical to your truth. I then asked you to circle any words from that list that aroused an emotional response in you, and that we'd be coming back to them. I would like to return to those words now and observe what feelings arose. Perhaps you noticed a jolt of fear or anger—maybe even a spasm of loathing or hatred. Let's dig into these emotional responses and understand why they welled up within us.

> *"What you resist not only persists, but will grow in size."*
> — **Carl Jung, founder of analytical psychology**

EXERCISE

Return to that list of "things I am not" from chapter three and examine the words that you circled. Write them again in the space below and then explain why they make you angry/upset/afraid/etc. Dive into the emotion behind the words. If you did not circle any items in the previous chapter, feel free to create a list of words that really "set you off." Try to delve into the "why" behind them.

The word _____ makes me feel _____
because I _____
_____
_____.

The word _____ makes me feel _____
because I _____
_____
_____.

The word _____ makes me feel _____ because I _____
_____
_____ .

The word _____ makes me feel _____ because I _____
_____
_____ .

The word _____ makes me feel _____ because I _____
_____
_____ .

> *"Darkness cannot drive out darkness; only light can do that."*
> — **Dr. Martin Luther King Jr.,**
> **civil right activist and minister**

We cannot carve out the sections of our identity that we do not like. When we try to surgically isolate or kill off parts of who we are—we end up deadening large swaths of our psyche. Returning to Brené Brown again, she says, "We cannot selectively numb emotions. When we numb the painful emotions, we also numb the positive emotions." If, for example, we try to cut off our sexuality because we believe our orientation to be unacceptable, we won't just sever that one part of ourselves. We will also destroy attributes that we desire to keep. We may end up sacrificing our ability to love, connect meaningfully with other people, share our authentic selves, express healthy emotions, accept tenderness, or feel valued. We risk becoming zombie-like—turning into not-fully-alive monsters staggering forward, clawing for life.

Until my early twenties, I was so thoroughly closeted that I even hid the truth of my orientation from myself. I closed off the knowledge that I might be same-sex attracted because it clashed with who I wanted to be and what I wanted out of life. I wanted to be a leading man in Hollywood—I wanted to be Batman. My younger mind decided that, in order to achieve this trajectory, it was critical for me to be straight. As I successfully convinced myself of my heteronormativity, I began to lose several key emotions. For many years, for example, I couldn't get angry. The fiery emotion of anger was simply intangible.

The ironic thing is that, by becoming an emotionally limited person, I actually hindered my ability to become a successful actor. At its essence, acting is a career where people are lauded for their ability to connect and project empathy. The very thing that I was doing in order to achieve my goal of success was, in hindsight, my biggest obstacle.

Interestingly, many people in my life applauded me for being so calm. They told me I was doing a good job for not getting angry—for denying myself from myself. Even though they saw my psychological self-coercion as a positive attribute, I recognized it as a serious problem. Even though I wasn't consciously aware of hiding my queerness, I was keenly cognizant of a big problem in my emotional processing. There were moments when rage should have justifiably arisen—witnessing cruelty, experiencing intense disappointment—and the fact that I could not respond was a road flare. I correctly guessed that if I couldn't feel critical emotions, there were likely to be other parts of myself that I'd suffocated as well. I suspected that I might be denying my own sexuality, even before I had any practical experiences to confirm such. I couldn't just selectively remove one section of who I was.

> *"Self-harm. The world will come at you with knives anyway—you do not need to beat them to it."*
> — **Caitlin Moran, English journalist and writer**

What are the uncomfortable truths that you're denying? You may not be able to put them into words yet—it took several years before I could name the sources of my distress. What might be possible, however, is to do what I did and notice the gaps where key elements of your identity are missing. When do you witness moments where emotions should be arising but aren't? Maybe you feel stoic when you should be crying (when experiencing the untimely death of a loved one, say), or perhaps you are vaguely unsettled when you should be elated (when your sister wins her dream job and an opportunity to travel the world). Where are the vacant holes in your life? They may turn out to be the keyholes that unlock the doors to your truer self.

EXERCISE

Let's turn our focus toward ourselves and moments that have caused us undue stress. What are some instances where you felt unjustifiably heightened emotions? When did you lash out at someone for a simple mistake? When did you cry despite only spilling a mug of coffee? When did you laugh while seeing someone get hurt?

_____

_____

_____

_____

_____

_____

_____

_____

_____

_____

What are some moments where you noticed a glaring lack of emotions? When was a time when you should have been celebrating, but you felt cold? When did everyone else weep, but you felt stone-hearted? When did everyone else gush, but you felt unmoved?

_____

_____

_____

_____

_____

_____

_____

_____

_____

_____

_____

_____

_____

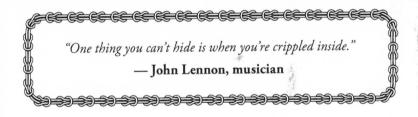

"One thing you can't hide is when you're crippled inside."
— John Lennon, musician

Whatever we deeply fear needs to be explored. Those shadowy monsters may not represent your whole truth—they may not even be a significant portion of your truth. But the sheer fact that you are having strong emotions (or lack of) is an indicator that there is meaningful work for you to explore here. The intense feelings and zones of apathy are spotlights shining onto areas that need compassion, need acceptance, and need love. We must strive to embrace all of our parts, not just the "nice" or "pretty" sections that are socially acceptable. In order to come into wholeness, we need to accept the entirety of our being.

There is terminology regarding these parts of ourselves that we don't want to acknowledge—they are called our "shadow sides." They are the sections that don't currently fit within the context of our public-facing life. Sometimes our shadows are huge, identity-altering topics like sexuality or gender. Sometimes they are smaller, less world-shifting curiosities like kinks, cravings for adrenaline-inspiring activities like skydiving, or unexplored fantasies pertaining to unicorns and forested cottages. If you discover that you have an unquenchable thirst for baking cupcakes—while it probably won't scandalize your mother—it is still important to acknowledge that desire and bring it into the boundaries of your conscious self. If the shadow is larger, or seemingly more profane (from your current perspective), it can take longer and require greater struggle to integrate.

The important thing to keep in mind is that this work eventually needs to come to fruition. To the extent that we feel ashamed of whatever lurks in the dark, we will continue to react irrationally and inappropriately—possibly causing greater harm and unhappiness to ourselves and others around us. "Anything that is repressed will express itself inappropriately." It's time to grab a shovel and a flashlight, and start exhuming the bodies we've buried in the basement of our minds.

I would like you to do a drawing depicting yourself as if all your worst fears proved correct. If you fully acknowledged all your naughty bits, your shameful sections, what would you look like? I encourage you to create a self-portrait (and it's okay if it ends up abstract) that highlights your greatest fears of who you *don't* want to be. If you highlight all your unlovable, unsavory, undesirable bits—what sort of picture emerges? Be brave—and see what shows up.

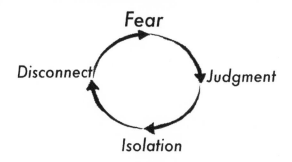

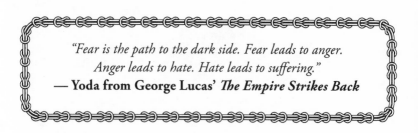

I would like to share with you what I call the "fear cycle." If we want to look at the process of how we become disconnected from our internal truth, our cosmic sense of wholeness, it is relevant to look at the steps that occur in that process. It begins with the amygdala portion of our brain reporting danger—and culminates in us actively pulling away from whatever is causing our distress.

Much like with Yoda's advice to Luke, fear is indeed the path to the "dark side." If we go back many thousand years to when we were still living in the African Savannah and trying to fend off hungry lions, fear would have been a very useful emotion. Fear keeps us safe, out of harm's way, and corralled in ways that promote survival. But within the context of the modern world, fear has become an overburdened emotion. Fear can keep us from speaking up when we see societal wrongs, from enacting something that feels important to our wellbeing, from trying that which has always enticed us. In fact, I would go as far as to argue that any decision made with fear being predominant will be wrong. And there is neuroscience to back this up.

When we enter a state of "fight-or-flight," the amygdala signals for the hypothalamus to release adrenaline and cortisol—stress hormones. The greater the level of stress, the more hormones are released. The amygdala also has the ability to co-opt other areas of the brain for processing power—effectively rendering them inert in regard to their usual tasks. This chemical process is known as "amygdala hijacking"—and what it entails is the intense reduction in our ability to make sound decisions. As our levels of stress climb—our fight-or-flight reactions increase—the less brain space we have available to think. We will choose wrong. We return to a less-evolved state of processing, where we rely predominantly upon impulse. And that impulse is to keep ourselves alive—not to make us long-term happy.

Our bodies and brains have evolved for survival, not for thriving. In earlier times, to make it through the night was success enough. But not in our modern world. We have to consciously train our brain to remain calm, to not respond so viscerally and dramatically to dangerous stimuli. One of the best tools for lasting fear-reduction for the brain is meditation—which is yet another reason why I opted to impart mindfulness practices early in the book. Studies have shown that the size of our amygdala can actually be changed with as little as eight weeks of regular meditation.[1]

Returning our focus to the fear cycle—when something inspires fear within us, our first response is to strive to understand what is going on. We dissect, label, and cast judgment. Now, there can be useful and beneficial judgment—like deciding when it is safe to dash across a busy street—but too often, our judgment is not helpful. We start categorizing stimuli as being positive or negative. What we are observing becomes good or bad, wicked or charitable, holy or sinful.

The danger is that when this judgment then reflects onto aspects of ourselves, we begin qualifying our innate natures. Instead of the source of our distress being simply positive or negative—we translate that same opinion to ourselves. Suddenly, *we* become the wicked ones, the sinful ones, the unholy. We initiate the process of distancing ourselves from ourselves—shaving off our loathsome bits.

Furthermore, our decisions on whether something is considered inherently good or wicked is based entirely on our previous experiences. All judgments are colored by our worldview up to this point. As we've already addressed in this book, very few things in the world are unequivocally good or bad—if you think something is good, I guarantee that there's another person out there who firmly believes the opposite.

Now, something might be dangerous—but danger isn't inherently negative. Stepping up to the front of a crowded room and delivering an acceptance speech is dangerous—but worth it. Deciding to welcome a child into your home through adoption is scary—but filled with love and rewards.

"There is nothing good nor bad, but thinking makes it so," advises Hamlet in Shakespeare's tragedy of the same name. We should be cautious about leaping to the conclusion that, because some instigator inspired fear within us, it should automatically be shunned or avoided. A homeowner might see a tree in his yard as beautiful because it provides shade—but his neighbor detests the plant for continually shedding leaves into his yard. The twenty-year-old student in Cancun might see their night of drunken frivolity as carefree fun—but their parents, watching the subsequent online videos, view their antics as short-sighted and career-wrecking. One person calls it an act of violent murder, while another defends it as righteous retribution. Perspective is everything—very little is objectively positive or negative.

Once the process of judging and qualifying is initiated, the source of our attention gets shoved into the "not so good" column and subsequently becomes diminished. It is no longer living, vital, complex—instead, it is flat, lifeless, and static. We box it in, so it feels less intimidating. By being reduced in potency through judgment, scary moments that could have taught meaningful lessons become happenings to be forgotten.

Moving on to step three. If you decide that some idea, object, or part of yourself is fearsome, and thereby label it as "negative," you will instinctually begin to separate yourself from it. This is what I dub as "isolation." You retreat from whatever you deemed to be "bad"—you erect walls to separate you from the source of your unease.

If whatever instigated your terror is reflected inside of you, there will only be so far that you can retreat before you have to start lopping off psychological pieces of your identity. You will have to forcibly disconnect from the parts that make you afraid. Whether it be your sexual identity, your body expression, your religion, your ethics—you will sever whatever sparked the fear-based reaction inside. This launches the fourth stage, "disconnection"—both from yourself and the outer world.

So, in summary: fear arises inside of you; you discern the cause and cast judgment on it (labeling it as negative), causing any "negative" traits reflected inside of you become isolated; and then you try to eliminate those qualities through disconnection. If fear arises again from similar stimuli, hitting upon the same source of unease inside, you will repeat the process, striving to distance yourself even further from those "unacceptable" bits of your psyche/identity.

Complex—but hopefully it makes sense.

It is critical to recognize that you felt an initial response of fear explicitly because some part of you either desired or resonated with whatever you were encountering. Some part of you identified with whatever scared you. Even if you consciously thought that it was wrong or not who you really are—some aspect of you felt called to connect with it. And that realization is terrifying to recognize and accept. You may have wanted to believe that you were only a certain way—but then a hidden, forbidden desire made you realize that you might be something else altogether.

As we work to embrace our shadows, it is important to recognize that none of us are entirely "good" people. None of us are pure sunshine, positive energy, and kittens all the time. Each of us has our basements filled with gargoyles that we don't want to acknowledge. We have to get past categorizing each part of ourselves as acceptable or unacceptable—we have to embrace all of our identity to come into being.

Shortly after turning thirty, I found myself freshly married, deeply in love with my spouse, and feeling really good about where I was headed in life. I had come a long way in my journey toward self-acceptance—I had moved away from Hollywood and was focusing my efforts on coming into intrinsic alignment. I was teaching yoga and meditation full-time, I had reconnected with childhood friends, and I was writing a blog on the topic of cultivating wholeness.

My husband and I were walking through a Whole Foods parking garage when he commented on a sarcastic comment that I had made moments prior. Two muscle-dudes had been loading up their carts with dozens of eggs and gallons of yogurt—and I made some holier-than-thou comment about their body insecurities.

"You know that you're judgmental because part of you wishes you could look like them," he said, giving me side-eye. He paused and then added thoughtfully, "I am okay with you exploring that if you feel like that's something you need to do. It seems like you've got some shadow work to do around this topic."

I was surprised—he was absolutely right. I had worked so hard to accept all my bright, shiny bits—to identify as this person who was all about "body positivity" and "loving yourself for where you're at" that I had shoved any feelings that were otherwise into my psychic basement. I had so identified with being wholesome, accepting, and overtly kind that I could not acknowledge the parts of me that were anything else. Somewhere inside of me was this primal, brutal, masculine energy banging to be released. My husband could tell that there were aspects of my identity that I was rejecting—that my out-of-character, caustic humor was a sign of internal disconnection.

There was a part of myself that I didn't want to listen to—a part of me that said, "I don't want to be a scrawny guy for all my life. I want to feel strong—I want to get huge. Screw all this self-acceptance bullshit—let's eat cow and lift heavy things." Taking a deep breath, I acknowledged it, accepted it, and opened the padlock to my muscle-building monsters. The next week, my exploration into my bro bodybuilder persona began. I dove into my shadow.

Even though I was mostly living in my truth as a positive-vibes, peace-loving sort of guy—there were ancillary bits of who I am that I wasn't acknowledging. Again, if something proves true, then so too does its opposite. We have both our light and our dark. I might generally be a generous person, but there are times when I am petty. I can strive to be kind and forgiving—but I have moments when I lash out. I can't entirely reject those parts of me. Both sides are integral to who I am—and by saying I was only light-seeking and well-adjusted, I was suppressing my shadow. I may not want to live on the dark side of the moon, but I have to acknowledge it exists. To think that we can somehow erase all our sinful, ugly, undesirable sections is insanity—we are human and will always have our foibles.

Generally, at that point in my life, I was feeling mostly contented with my fit-but-thin body. When I was younger, however, that was not the case. I used to get picked on a lot for being too effeminate and slender. Peers and some less-than-kind family members would call me "anorexic" or "toothpick." There were parts of my psyche that wanted to compensate for that pain, parts of me that wanted to revel in unadulterated testosterone and prove that I could be man-enough, that I could take up space, that I was worthy of being seen.

Over the next year, I dove into the muscle-building lifestyle. I ate six meals a day, I took trips to the gym each morning and afternoon, and I even explored supplements of questionable legality. I became fixated on becoming as huge as possible as a way of compensating for those years of feeling inferior. Soon, my desire for growth outpaced my biological abilities. I was fantasizing about gaining fifty pounds of bulk—then, one-hundred pounds of lean mass. The more I focused on this goal, the more I was determined to not let anything get in my way. I became obsessed. It was all I could think about, dream about. I stopped creating art. It became the center of my life.

Over ten months, I managed to pack on more than two-dozen pounds—people were now calling me a "beast," and I adored the attention. It was the first time in my life that anyone had seen me in that way—perceived me as being sufficiently manly. I was exploring my shadow to its fullest, and while it was exhilarating, it became clear that I had lost my tether to my ordinary self. I had fully entered the basement and had no intentions of climbing out.

> *"I know that you're afraid of drag. I wonder if it's more that you're afraid of what your wife will think and your children—or if it's that you'll love it so much that you won't come back."*
> — **RuPaul Charles, drag queen and entrepreneur**

Sometimes, we dive into the thing we've always feared—and, because it's so foreign and holds such an illicit appeal, it can be hard to find our way back. I moved fully into a side of myself that was the exact opposite of my sensitive, self-accepting normal life. Though I couldn't realize it at that time, I had developed muscle dysmorphia—or what some call "bigorexia." No matter how muscular I got, it wasn't enough. Like a skeletally-thin, bulimic person thinking that they are still overweight—I still thought I was too scrawny. No matter how big I grew, my desires grew commensurately. I was already spending outside my means on excess meals and supplements—I was only a short step away from using steroids to achieve my never-fulfillable ambitions.

My husband observed all this with wary concern. He wanted to give me the space to explore what I felt I needed to in order to heal—but he kept dropping hints that I purposefully ignored. That is until one day, while we were vacationing in Manhattan and walking through Central Park, he gave me an ultimatum.

"It seems like you've really been enjoying this growth journey," he said, "but it's been taking up all of your energy and focus. You haven't been writing; you haven't been making art. I married you a year ago because of you being this compassionate, creative, kind, soulful man. And while this whole "getting swole" thing might be *part* of your identity—I don't think it's the whole of you. Heck, I don't think it's even the majority—but you've been living as if it were your all.

"I want you to know (and I mean this with all compassion) that this isn't the man I wanted to marry. If this is who you want to be, I will support and love you; but I will need to do so from a distance. I don't want to be partnered to someone who is investing all their life-force into this one pursuit. I want more from life—I want to help people. And I thought you wanted the same.

"If you stay on this path—I will leave you."

I stopped, took a deep breath, and looked out into the New York skyline. He was absolutely correct. I had lost my way. Being so afraid of this part of me for so long had made me overcompensate—I went too far. It was time for me to return to wholeness...and bring what I learned back with me.

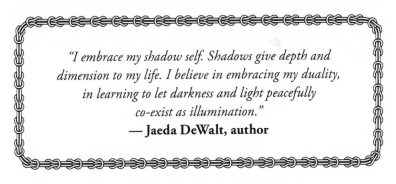

"I embrace my shadow self. Shadows give depth and dimension to my life. I believe in embracing my duality, in learning to let darkness and light peacefully co-exist as illumination."
— Jaeda DeWalt, author

For many of us, the fear that our shadow sides will entrance us so thoroughly that we will not be able to separate from them is what keeps us from exploring them in the first place. The parts that we don't want to be true, the doors we are afraid to open—we feel dread at the notion that we will open the door and never be able to close it again. That it will become our new reality.

Sometimes these fears prove valid. Sometimes we learn things about ourselves that we can never un-learn. Sexuality, for example—if you realize that your orientation is different than you assumed, that you profoundly love someone of a different gender than your current partner, that can be a challenging reckoning to face. Sometimes, however, our shadows are just areas we dip into from time to time—they remain occasional respites from our ordinary existences.

Sometimes, what we discover during shadow exploration actually proves to be realizations of what we are not. Once we explore the illicit, it loses its dark appeal, and we no longer find it tantalizing. The person who spends their early-adulthood entirely celibate might discover that they need to spend a few years being promiscuous before they're ready to settle down. The kid who was never allowed to go to parties might find that they're out all night swinging glow-sticks—before they're ready to realize that they actually prefer quiet gatherings. Saint Augustine had a wild and tumultuous few decades before he was prepared to mellow out into sainthood. Life requires balance, and we need to find that within ourselves and within whatever areas we feel called to explore.

A pendulum has to swing to both extremes before it can settle in the middle—and so too must our self-expression. The trouble comes when it gets stuck on one end. I had developed an infatuation with my shadow—and my husband became a lifeline to reel me back. He reminded me that I have to hold *all* parts of who I am—the light and the dark. He supported me through the process of integrating my shadow-self with my full identity. He anchored me in my truth and guided me back to my home.

Healthy exploration is advisable and entirely necessary to release the pressure-valve, so to speak—but we eventually need to be able to hold all aspects of ourselves. We cannot live in the extremes. "The middle path is the way to wisdom," says the mystic poet, Rumi. We should neither overly-embrace nor reject the bits that have caused us shame. It's the Hindu principle of *Santosha:* contentment with what is—no pushing or pulling. Just simply allowing things to be as they are.

I eventually came back to a state of balance where—while bulkier than I was before this adventure—I learned to approach my appreciation of size with a deep acceptance of the beauty of being where I am. Through the process of going on my shadow journey, I gained an invaluable knowledge about myself, my desires, and the monsters that lurk inside my closets. If I had never explored my suppressed side, I would have always felt haunted. Those secret desires would have lurked under the bed, hid inside the attic. Without this journey, I would have always wondered what might have been. Now, I can hold the light and the dark. I can be wildly self-accepting—and, at the same time, push myself at the gym and drink protein shakes. I am healthier, more integrated, and more self-fulfilled than I ever was before. I follow the middle path.

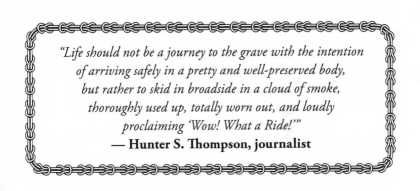

"Life should not be a journey to the grave with the intention of arriving safely in a pretty and well-preserved body, but rather to skid in broadside in a cloud of smoke, thoroughly used up, totally worn out, and loudly proclaiming 'Wow! What a Ride!'"
— **Hunter S. Thompson, journalist**

It doesn't matter how long you try to run from that which you cannot ignore—you will never travel far enough. You will have to face your subconscious needs eventually. There is no outpacing our desires. We can suppress them for a while—decades even—but eventually, they will erupt from the ground like angry zombies. That's when marriages fail, parents abandon their children, friends destroy friends—there's a force buried inside that is fighting its way free. Perhaps your shadow has to do with selfishness or needing to explore reckless adventures. Heck, maybe it's about wanting to know what it's like to live as a rodeo clown. Now is your chance to name your longings as best as your able and face them head-on.

It's important to acknowledge that we never know our subconscious in its entirety—there are too many layers, too many craggy depths. But we should do the best we can to climb into the wells that we find—all the while, being sure that we have a strong lifeline rooted to the ground above. As you begin exploring your shadows, it's critical to have a confidant who will ensure your safety, make sure you stay tethered to your regular life.

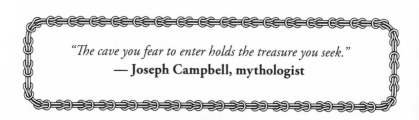

"The cave you fear to enter holds the treasure you seek."
— **Joseph Campbell, mythologist**

EXERCISE

We've been dancing around this for a while now. I want you to be bold and strive to name your fears. Risk exploring the deepest, scariest parts of you—and know that it's going to be okay. You don't need to "do" anything about what you disclose here, but you do need to admit to yourself what you're really feeling. It's alright, I promise. You'll feel much better once you can name that nagging bit in the back of your brain that has kept you awake. Speaking and writing your truth can have immense power. This is part of what has been holding you back from achieving your full potential in life. Be brave.

The part about myself that I fear, that I don't want to acknowledge but keep wondering about, is....

_____

_____

_____

_____

_____

_____

_____

_____

_____

_____

_____

If there is something that feels forbidden—but it keeps intriguing you—it may be useful to safely and openly explore it. I encourage you to undertake such expeditions with enthusiasm and also caution. Be wary of harming those who you love and support—make sure you get enthusiastic consent from anyone these actions might possibly affect, especially if you are in intimate relationships with them.

Things that I would like to explore, but have always frightened me, are...

_____

_____

_____

_____

_____

_____

_____

_____

_____

_____

What are some ways I could safely try them while keeping me and my loved ones protected?

_____

_____

_____

_____

_____

_____

_____

_____

_____

_____

> *"Afraid that our inner light will be extinguished or our inner darkness exposed, we hide our true identities from each other. In the process, we become separated from our own souls. We end up living divided lives, so far removed from the truth we hold within that we cannot know the integrity that comes from being what you are."*
> — **Parker J. Palmer, author**

As stated prior, we cannot selectively disconnect—we cannot selectively numb. When we try to distance ourselves from whatever emotions we dislike—lust, anger, shame, etc.—we disconnect from parts like joy, gratitude, intimacy, inner peace. To fully reconnect with our inner truth, we have to embrace every aspect of us.

By exploring the parts of our psyches that we never wanted to see, we will shine a bright light on our authentic selves. You wanted to be on this journey toward knowing your integral, spiritual identity? Good. Here's the big step: learn to love yourself, warts and all. None of us are faultless—all of us have our baggage, our incongruous bits, our shadows. You are a far harsher critic of your desires than anyone else will ever be. Let go and trust that this is part of your journey—this is what you are here to do.

EXERCISE

You just wrote about the things you fear but have secretly wanted to try—but have you actually done them? Perhaps it's time to leave the house, get in the car or on a train, and strap on your parachute. Again, act wisely and obtain consent from those affected—but experiment with that thing that has always tantalized you. Once you do, journal about your experience below.

How I felt while exploring my shadow-side:

_____
_____
_____
_____
_____
_____
_____
_____
_____
_____

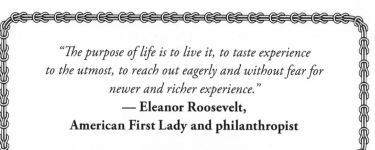

As you go on this journey of the "dark night of the soul," I want to encourage you to share your findings with people who you deeply trust. Not everyone has earned a right to hear your stories—and some stories should be shared with perhaps only one or two key individuals. We are tiptoeing through hallowed and sacred ground now—we need to be delicate of sharing our truths with those who will support our findings and hold us through the inevitable challenges.

As the storyteller, Carmen Agra Deedee, says, "There are stories you tell from stages. There's stories that you may tell in a small group of people with some good wine. And there's stories you tell late at night to a friend, maybe once in your life. And then there are stories that we whisper into a Stygian darkness." Know who has earned the right to hear your shadow stories—seek out those who will love and support you through anything you might encounter.

It is important that you have a sturdy lifeline; that may take the form of a devoted partner, a therapist, a priest, or a mentor. Be kind to yourself and your process by establishing a proactive relationship with someone who holds your best interests at heart and has proved their ability to hold discordant experiences with grace. The support and insights of my husband during my own time of self-exploration proved invaluable.

Lastly, once the journey to the realm of shadow has reached a pausing point (because it never fully ends), and you have integrated what you've learned—be conscientious of what you share about your identity and with whom. If you are going to irreparably harm those you care about by sharing what you discovered in the realm of shadow, it may be wise to be selective about who and what you disclose. Perhaps only a select few have earned the privilege of knowing your whole story. Perhaps you exclaim your findings on social media. The choice is yours regarding how transparent or open you want to be. Be honest—be compassionate and kind.

> *"The most beautiful people we have known are those who have known defeat, known suffering, known struggle, known loss, and have found their way out of the depths. These persons have an appreciation, a sensitivity, and an understanding of life that fills them with compassion, gentleness, and a deep loving concern. Beautiful people do not just happen."*
>
> — **Elisabeth Kübler-Ross, psychologist and death researcher**

SUMMARY:

— We all have dark sides we don't want to acknowledge; parts that are ugly, unkind, or not socially permissible.

— You cannot outrun the shadow; be brave and face it head-on.

— Identify your support network, be open and accountable to anyone your actions might affect, and integrate your discoveries mindfully.

Chapter 5:

RAINBOWS AND PECULIAR ROADS

"We're all mad here. I'm mad. You're mad."
"How do you know I'm mad?" asked Alice.
"You must be," replied the Cheshire Cat,
"Because you're here, and everyone here is mad."
— ***Alice in Wonderland* by Lewis Carroll**

You, my intrepid reader, are probably queer.

Did that sentence make your stomach lurch? "Oh, no! The author thinks that I might be queer—or worse yet, he thinks *everyone* is queer (clutches pearls)!"

Well, yes...and no. I *do* think each and every one of us is unique—a little odd, a little kooky, possibly abnormal—queer, in the etymological sense. And that's a good thing—we need to celebrate our differences and own our quirks. "If you're always trying to be normal you will never know how amazing you can be," says poet Maya Angelou.

Until we can learn to revel in our oddities, we will forever be slaves to conforming to the desires of the populous. We will never be memorable or authentic—we will just be bland, boring reiterations of everyone else. What makes you different makes you beautiful, and it should be celebrated.

But you were correct in your initial guess—that isn't *really* the type of queer I'm addressing in this chapter. Chances are very good that if you've made it this far into *Journey to the Ecstatic Self*, there's something about my words that speak to you—our energies resonate in some way. Just like tuning forks vibrating at complimentary frequencies, we are in harmony.

Do you know who I am most in harmony with? Other queer people.

When I was in high school, I had a couple of close friends—and all of us identified as straight, heteronormative kids from the suburbs. At that time, it wasn't clear what brought us together. As the years passed, however, and we migrated into our twenties—we realized through successive coming-out posts that each one of us had been secretly closeted. Even though we hadn't consciously known that anyone else in our group identified as anything other than a zero on the Kinsey spectrum (totally heterosexual), all us queer kids found one another.

In the same way, I can now walk into a crowded room and usually know within a few seconds who are the other LGBTQ+ people—without them saying, doing, or acting in any way overt. I *resonate* with them in a specific way—and when we talk, our interactions feel more substantial and fruitful (pardon the pun).

Perhaps you are one-hundred-percent heteronormative—but if my story has been speaking to you, if you have felt compelled to keep reading—you probably aren't. I'll let you in on a little secret, though: nearly everyone is non-heteronormative in some way.

> *"You look ridiculous if you dance. You look ridiculous if you don't dance. So you might as well dance."*
> — **Gertrude Stein, American writer and queer icon**

I will explain this bold assertion in just a few paragraphs—but first, a story on how I came to accept my own queerness.

Going back to my high school experiences, I opted out of many of the traditional coming-of-age rites so I could keep up my facade of heteronormativity. I never dated anyone—but neither did my fellow closeted peers. We found solace in one another's platonic company—and being part of a celibate group meant that I didn't feel too odd for ignoring romantic pursuits.

I had a sense that I was attracted to men, but that desire didn't register within the narrow confines of what I understood sexual burgeoning to mean. In the stories I heard, heterosexual attraction was always described as a gift that was all-of-a-sudden bestowed on a young man—boys would go from viewing their female classmates as purely platonic friends to abruptly seeing them as boobs and butts with an outline of a person in between. I hoped that one day I would wake up and spontaneously find women arousing. I imagined an eroticized version of the Tooth Fairy floating about, eagerly waiting to exchange childhood innocence for sexual interest—and maybe she'd gotten hung up at the neighbor's.

Another rite of passage of which I opted out was alcohol consumption—my friends and I were strictly sober. While it's biologically healthy for young people to defer imbibing until their brains are fully matured (studies show that brain growth slows—and in some instances stops altogether—if people drink before their mid-twenties), my decision to abstain came from a deep fear of what would happen if I relaxed my self-control.[1] I was scared to see who would emerge if I ever lost my grip on the persona I effortfully projected into the world.

I was so focused on projecting a straight, hetero-and-masculine-normative presence that I staunched any sense of authentic selfhood. I believed that my will was like a blacksmith's iron hammer: I could use it to forge my identity, my body, and my mind into whatever shapes I wanted. So long as I kept a firm grip on willfulness, I could beat myself into being the man of my dreams.

All told, my friends and I were the sober, celibate nerds who signed up for too many clubs, partook in too many volunteer projects, and overloaded ourselves with too many collegiate-level classes. In the words of Rob Bell, "Busy is a drug that many people are addicted to"—and we were certainly hopped up on busy. We maintained a state of overwrought-ness so we wouldn't have the mental capacity to examine ourselves, our longings, and our buried desires. It's so much easier to delude one's self when you don't have the time or space to reflect, breathe, or simply sit still.

As we headed to our respective universities, I kept up my strict, regimented lifestyle. I never went to parties—and on the handful of exceptions when I did, I never drank. I maintained a relentlessly overbooked schedule so that I couldn't see how unhappy I really was. When you're rushing from your audit-only class (because you've maxed out your for-credit course-load), to the gym, to a midnight rehearsal, and then three hours of sleep—it's hard to wonder if you are living a life you actually want. You're too tired and trying too hard to simply make it through to the next day.

I also continued my practice of non-dating—I only asked out three women in my entire four years of college, all of whom I knew would say "no" (one actually laughed in my face when I asked her out). By setting myself up for rejection, I could say that I at least tried. I emerged from Northwestern more tightly wound than ever before.

Moving into my early twenties, I began to identify as asexual—not attracted to anyone. True, I did surreptitiously masturbate to images of (mostly) men—but I justified it in my head as a desire to look like them. I told myself that I wanted to be more masculine, more muscular, more well hung. It wasn't about *them*, I told myself—it was about me imagining myself as being a monstrously jacked himbo.

I wondered if I just had a low sexual appetite. Other people seemed inexorably pulled to their fellow humans—but I was so emotionally blocked that I felt nothing in regard to other living, breathing beings—only their pictures. I had my pin-up fantasies onscreen, but I wondered if something was wrong with me where I couldn't connect with real folks. I questioned if there were such a thing as being auto-sexual—romantically attracted to a hyper-sexualized version of your own self.

I had moved into the ashram by this point—and while there was a large part of me that came wanting to connect with my spiritual side and know my cosmic-self better, there was another part of me that wanted to avoid the messiness of the world. By moving directly from my university apartment to the yogic commune, I was able to avoid late-night rendezvous with roommates, unplanned discoveries at drunken karaoke, or spontaneous and amorous interactions one stumbles into on a dark and lonely evening. I chose rigid structure, isolation, and nearly monastic life to keep me from fully exploring myself and my desires.

I had hidden my same-sex attraction so thoroughly that I no longer knew where or what it was. But I was curious to know what was wrong with me—I wanted to feel like I was living a whole, integrated life. Furthermore, a person can only stay in a state of heightened control for so long before their willfulness fatigues. Even the strongest arm can keep the hammer raised at shoulder-height for only a specific length of time. My stamina was wearing out—I couldn't suppress my truth for much longer.

The first cracks appeared shortly before my twenty-fifth birthday. I was completing a year-long conservatory at The Second City—home of comedy giants—when a classmate and I became friends. He was a pickup artist, and he insisted on taking me under his wing—teaching me tricks of the trade to get me laid. He boasted that I couldn't possibly know what I wanted until I actually tried it. I needed to have sex, he convinced me—I was long past due.

After a few sessions of his swaggering instruction, I returned home to the ashram and found a fellow resident studying alone in the dining room. We had been friendly for a few years—and there had always been the faintest trace of a spark between us when we interacted. I pulled out the chair beside her and took a seat; I then casually offered her a foot massage. This swiftly turned into an invitation to my small bedroom—and ten minutes later, we were chest to chest on my bed, my hands reaching along the curves of her back.

I was excited to discover that I was becoming tepidly aroused in my nether-regions, but it was obvious to me that I wasn't passionately enjoying the experience—and neither was she. After a few moments of stroking and kissing, we mutually agreed that this was not what we wanted. We parted ways, and after a long, contemplative shower where I tried to wash my frustration, confusion, and remorse down the drain, I walked back out to the dining room to discover her with her laptop open and a dating site on her screen. She looked at me and smiled.

"I'm creating a dating profile for you," she said.

"Oh, really?" I replied, drying my hair and crossing toward her. The screen glowed with magenta and cobalt blue—I saw a picture of myself filling a bubble on the left-hand side.

"Yes, and I'm—" She paused and eyed me, considering. "I'm going to say that you're bisexual, and I want you to explore it."

I remember my mouth opening and my heartbeat zooming. I wanted to tell her, "no." I wanted to demur, to assert that there was no way that I was attracted to men. But I couldn't.

A few weeks prior, I had been shooting a romantic comedy feature film. In the movie, I played one-half of a gay couple—one of the principal roles. Late one night on set, I realized that I was feeling sexually attracted to my costar. He was an out, gay man—and we had become friends during our time together. I had opened up to him about my fears and lack of understanding in regard to my own sexuality, and he had likewise shared and connected with me about his own explorations. I had come to feel safe with him, and I recognized an emotional resonance between us. I think he was the first man to allow me to feel safe enough for my attraction to openly surface. It was perhaps the first (dare I even call it "seminal") time that I could openly and authentically admit to myself that I was turned-on by another man.

"Okay," I told my roommate. "I'll try it. But you've got to pretend to be me and set me up on a few dates. I'm too scared to talk for myself."

She agreed, and a few days later, I was sitting down for coffee at a café with a student who was about to graduate from The University of Chicago. The date didn't go very well, but it was the beginning of my romantic odyssey. Over the next several months, I met up with three or four different men or women per week—usually just for a cup of tea or a walk along the lakeshore—to learn more about who and to what

I was attracted. It was the beginning of me coming to terms with my orientation, my identity, and letting go of the image of the person I needed to be in order for my truer self to arise from the depths.

> *"Whenever people act like gay images in the media will influence kids to be gay, I want to remind them that gay children grew up with only straight people on television."*
> — **Ellen DeGeneres, comedian and queer icon**

When I came out, I remember certain family members asking, "Why is sexuality such a big deal? Why should it matter who you love or who you are attracted to? We (heteronormative people) don't talk about our sexuality all the time—how come you need to let everyone know? Why is it so important?"

Well, A) you exist in a culture where your orientation is consistently and overtly discussed (notice all the hyper-sexualized ads, the endless succession of heterosexually amorous songs on the radio, and the ever-present romantic "B-plots" in films featuring straight characters). B) you don't need to talk about it because you've never been made to feel different or shameful for the way you are.

Even growing up in openly-affirming, inclusive environments, young queer people still subconsciously know that there is something that separates them from the rest of their pack. Even if they can't name what it is, they know there is something that demarcates them as different—an off-pitch resonance between them and the rest of the world.

We learn from an early age—largely due to our survival instincts—to be suspicious of anything foreign. Whatever is unlike what we've previously experienced might be dangerous, or at least threatening. We internalize that wariness and hold it against ourselves—we believe that there is something fundamentally wrong about us because we are different from the heteronormative culture that makes up the bulk of society. We learn that we are the outsiders, the dangerous ones.

Growing up queer in a straight world is a forcible encouragement for a young person to start disassociating from themselves. Since you are reading a book on the topic of connecting with your essence, there is a high likelihood that you've encountered an analogous stressor in your young life that caused a wedge within yourself. Nearly every person I've met in the LGBTQ+ community has struggled to overcome some level of self-denial. So, if this is an ongoing issue for you—while there's a chance you might be entirely heteronormative—chances are excellent that you are a little bit queer in some way.

The term "queerness"—and why I choose to use it—can encapsulate so many different things. With our current cultural understanding, there are four main spectrums of sex, gender identity, gender expression, and orientation that can articulate the myriad ways that a person can be queer.

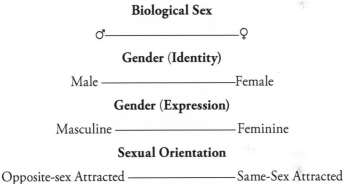

Biological Sex

♂———————————♀

Gender (Identity)

Male ———————————Female

Gender (Expression)

Masculine ——————————— Feminine

Sexual Orientation

Opposite-sex Attracted ——————————— Same-Sex Attracted

I consciously choose to describe this as our "current" understanding because our sociological interpretations of gender, sexual expression, and sexual orientation are ever-evolving. What we believed even twenty years ago is not what we believe today. Also, as a cisgender, male-presenting, omnisexual (but mostly gay) man—I do not have as nuanced of a vocabulary as many of my beautifully rainbowed siblings. I in no way consider myself the expert in queerness, nor as having lived the most radically exploratory queer existence. What I share here is simply a launching-off point in regard to exploring identity diversity.

This is only my understanding of the spectrums; it in no way claims to be exhaustive or "right." It is simply a perspective—one of many.

Turning to the various spectrums—in the first row, we have biological sex. That could pertain to the presence or absence of vaginas and/or penises, ovaries and/or testes, breasts and non-breasts, etc. It also encompasses possible sex chromosome combinations. One's sex identification can be changed with a purposeful shift in gender identification (such as through gender reassignment surgery)—but the two spectrums are not necessarily in lockstep.

The next spectrums both relate to gender. They encompass how we see ourselves, our roles in society, and what gender we externally present as being. The first (identity) pertains to how our minds or identities align with either/both/neither gender—the second (expression) is the outward trappings associated with gender that we project to the world.

There are a whole lot of variables that go into these two spectrums, varying from how a person cognitively experiences their own mind, to their relationship to their body, to how masculine or feminine they feel or enact. Whether they choose he/him pronouns, she/her, or they/them—there's a lot of room for overlap and (what can seem like) contradiction within these two spectrums.

> "I don't identify as transgender. But I'm clearly gender-not-normal. I don't think even lesbian is the right identity for me. I really don't. I might as well come out now. I identify as tired. I'm just tired."
> — **Hannah Gadsby, comedian and storyteller**

The fourth row concerns the people to whom you are attracted: men, women, neither, both, gender non-binary people, or something different altogether. Do you prefer to couple with one person, two or more—do you identify as being attracted to someone's personality more than their gender? Terms like bisexual, omnisexual, pansexual, asexual, polyamorous, demisexual all come into play—there is quite the variety here, too.

To show how these four spectrums could relate to an individual person, let's take, for example, a straight dude—or, more aptly, a heterosexual, gender-conforming, cisgender man. He would be far to the left on each of the four spectrums: male sex organs, male-identifying, masculine-presenting, heterosexual. A hyper-feminine lesbian woman would fall on the far right in each spectrum—whereas a butch lesbian might be to the far right except for the one spectrum of gender presentation (more to the middle-left, there). A gender-fluid or nonbinary person who presents as androgynous and identifies as pansexual would fall somewhere in the center of each line.

Since there are so many combinations possible within these spectrums, doesn't it seem unlikely that ninety-five percent of the world would fall neatly into the purely cisgender, gender-normative, heterosexual ends, as some statisticians suggest?[2] And these four spectrums are actually more nuanced and complex than they seem at an initial glance.

Beginning with the spectrum pertaining to biological sex, one might assume that there are just two sexes—men and women. If a baby is born male, slap a blue diaper on his bottom and wheel him off to the nursery. If she is female, tie a pink bonnet around her head and send her to the kitchen to learn cooking and cleaning skills. Right?

Not quite. A newborn's sex might not be simple to define. According to the Accord Alliance, approximately one out of every one-thousand-five-hundred births involve a child with atypical genitalia (that may sound like very few, but that equates to over five *million* individuals in today's global population).[3] These intersex children don't just have either testes/penises or vagina/ovaries—they have a more unique combination or configuration.

Further, there are countless children born with sex chromosomes that may or may not match their genital expression. Most often, chromosomes pair together in one of two ways: XX (typically assigned female) and XY (typically assigned male)—but there are untold others who go about their lives with other possible combinations (XXY, XYY, XXX, etc.). Since most Americans do not currently receive genetic testing, many have no clue that they, genetically speaking, fall into a different camp than they assume.

Next, let's turn to the two spectrums pertaining to gender. When I was young, I had a close friend who, using the terminology of that time, was a "tomboy"—a female-identified person who dressed and acted in more traditionally masculine ways. While some might have assumed that she would eventually identify as lesbian or transgender, this wasn't the case for her. Despite her gender-non-conforming appearance and demeanor, she is a straight, cisgender woman, today. The four spectrums are not necessarily correlated—and non-traditional placement within one does not necessarily go hand in hand with another. Gender-atypical behavior/presentation is not indicative of sexuality, gender identification, or biological sex.

For myself, when I was young, I was often called a "sissy" for engaging with the things typically associated with girls like art, creativity, music, caretaking, and emotional sensitivity. While there were a few times when my gender expression dabbled with overt femininity—wearing my mother's nightgown or frolicking down the hall in Dorothy's ruby slippers—I mostly stayed within the boundaries of traditionally male-associated gender presentation.

As an adult, I identify as a cisgender male who is predominately same-sex attracted—but such a description doesn't capture the nuance of how I understand myself and my place in the world. Many of my role models and friends are women. When I watch a film or read a book, I many times prefer a female protagonist; several of my favorite musicians are bisexual women. Though I present as masculine, the way my mind perceives the world and identifies is more gender-neutral. At the same time, I so enjoy being in a man's body—the aesthetics of my muscles, sexual organs, and shape overall gives me great pleasure. So, with gender presentation, I am far to the masculine side—but gender identity, I am a little more toward the middle.

Someone who speaks beautifully on the topic of gender-not-normal-ness is the comedian Hannah Gadsby. Her remarkable stand-up performance, *Nanette*, tackles the nuances and challenges of being non-traditionally-gendered. She breaks down the prejudice that society maintains against individuals who present or behave outside of their assigned roles. She is able to heartbreakingly share her trauma while simultaneously making the audience laugh about the absurdity of their viewpoints.

> *"And he said, 'Oh, no, I get it. You're a lady-faggot. I'm allowed to beat the shit out of you,' and he did! He beat the shit out of me, and nobody stopped him. [...] And that is what happens when you soak one child in shame and give permission to another to hate. And that was not homophobia, pure and simple, people. That was gendered. If I'd been feminine, that would not have happened."*
> — **Hannah Gadsby in *Nanette*, 2018**

There are endless ways to express one's gender—there is no right way to enact masculinity or femininity. It is up to us to choose what feels right based on our desires, experiences, and environments. One of the things for which I applaud Generation Z is their willingness to aggressively break down traditional gender barriers and stereotypes. They prove that it is possible to be a butch woman and still wear lipstick and heels; it's possible to be a femme man and yet be tatted up and stomping around in combat boots. Gender identity, expression, and sex do not need to align in any coherent way. What someone feels, how they present, and how they identify can all clash in a beautiful cacophony.

This is the reasoning behind why people offer their preferred pronouns when introducing themselves (he/him/his, she/her/hers, they [or ze]/them/theirs)—it is a way to acknowledge that someone's gender identity may or may not reflect their external presentation. Again, my knowledge on this topic is in no way exhaustive—and how we, as a culture, talk about gender and sex is continually evolving. Please feel free to consult additional resources for a deeper understanding of the topic.

Lastly, let's turn to the fourth spectrum: sexuality. Many decades ago, society said that there were only two options—same or oppo-site-sex attracted. Or, to use more dated terminology, homosexual and heterosexual. Then, society became a little more accepting of the notion of bisexuality—which eventually led to a plethora of other possibilities. Some current terminology includes pansexual (attracted to individuals, not specific genders), asexual (attracted to no gender), demisexual (only attracted after establishing emotional connection), omnisexual (attracted to all genders for different reasons), sapiosexual (only attracted if an intellectual connection is present), among many others. Additionally, there are countless individuals who defy any sort of labeling.

According to Gallup—only four and a half percent of Americans identify as being in the LGBTQ+ community.[2] But there may be more to this story than there seems at first glance. For example, Gallop admits that Americans generally estimate that around a quarter of the population is queer—which gives us insight into what people might secretly know about their loved ones, information that they might not be self-reporting. More tellingly, a recent poll YouGov released in 2020 showed that a whopping 48% of both Generation Z and Millennials identify as something other than "completely heterosexual."[4] Consider that for a moment. Of the younger generations who have grown up in an era of relaxed mores around sexuality—nearly half of them say that they are not entirely straight.

Sure, perhaps some of them are still exploring their identities—that is entirely possible. But it is also highly likely that there are many in the "completely heterosexual" camp who have desires that they are yet unwilling to articulate. Is it possible that the larger populous overall is more queer than traditional polling suggests? Might we all, in fact, be a little bit queer?

When we examine the endless configurations of possible orientations and identities within the four spectrums, how likely does it seem that ninety-five percent of the world will be entirely cisgender, completely gender-conforming, and thoroughly heterosexual? Given the countless stories I've heard from straight-acting, gender-normal people—often whispered in moments of long-fought admittance—I think there are many who resonate in some way with the opposite ends of the four spectrums. I have personally encountered numerous stories divulged to me of secret desires that have been locked into proverbial attics due to societal or familial demands. Too few have felt empowered to live their personal truths—too many have boxed themselves into identities that do not feel genuine.

Queer individuals have faced discrimination, have been told (even if only in quiet or off-handed ways) that they are unlovable or imperfect—and they need to rewrite this programming. The world needs your diversity in order to thrive. You might be queer—you might not—but as we explored in the previous chapter, until you can own all parts of your identity, radically accepting your whole self will be nearly impossible. Fear of our sexuality, sex, gender presentation, or gender expression can be catalysts for disconnection. So, we actively work to let that anxiety go and blossom into self-acceptance.

"I believe that telling our stories, first to ourselves and then to one another and the world, is a revolutionary act. It is an act that can be met with hostility, exclusion, and violence. It can also lead to love, understanding, transcendence, and community. I hope that my being real with you will help empower you to step into who you are and encourage you to share yourself with those around you."
— **Janet Mock, writer and transgender activist**

EXERCISE

Our personal understanding of gender, biological sex, and sexuality are ever-deepening within ourselves. I, for example, have relabeled my orientation numerous times. When I was in my early twenties and highly sexually repressed, I identified as asexual. While I was attracted to images on screens, I was unable to feel a commensurate sense of longing to real people. Then, after I started dating, I experimented with calling myself bisexual, which soon turned into gay. That label stuck for a few years, until a trip I took across the ocean with a dear friend of mine.

She and I had been in each other's lives for several years—and we loved each other immensely. One night, she asked if it would be alright if we disrobed in front of each other. I felt totally comfortable with her proposal—but when she proceeded to frolic around our shared hotel room totally in the buff, I began to realize that my identity as being thoroughly same-sex attracted was no longer accurate. After two days of flouncing bosoms, I had to carefully admit that I was feeling turned on—and, after assuring her that my husband would probably prefer for us not to consummate that attraction, we agreed to keep our clothes mostly on.

This was a moment where my current identity label wasn't serving me. But moments like this happen more often than not—we all encounter situations that make us reconsider our self-definitions. After this experience abroad, I began to admit that there were still experiences where I was turned on by bodies that weren't overtly masculine. More recently, I have adopted the term omnisexual, since it seems encompassing of any possible attraction regardless of sex, gender presentation, or identification.

I have found trans men arousing—as well as trans women. I have

127

found cisgender women attractive—and men too. I am learning to embrace that any definition I give myself might be challenged by unexpected circumstances and uniquely beautiful individuals.

When was the last time you experienced an interaction where your usual labels didn't seem to fit? We are all one thing...until we find ourselves in a moment when, for whatever reason, suddenly we are not. Even if you are usually very "x," there have undoubtedly been times where you felt a little bit "y." From this angle, I think many will agree that there are at least times when we are all a bit queer.

In the space below, explore moments in your life where your gender/sex/sexuality experiences were outside of either yours or society's norms. We are intensely complex, layered creatures. The more that you accept that self-expression cannot be tidily tucked into a single compartment, the more at ease you'll be with yourself. So, in what ways are you odd, queer, or altogether different?

Stories of my queerness:

_____
_____
_____
_____ _____
_____
_____
_____
_____
_____
_____
_____
_____
_____
_____
_____
_____
_____

MEDITATION VI

Find a comfortable, relaxing body position. Close your eyes and bring your mind's eye down to the center of your hips—the space near the insertion point of the genitals. Yogis call this area the *svadhishthana chakra,* or the center of your sexual energy.

It is an area that is associated with the element of water. Everything is fluid, moving, changing. Even the organs in this area involve wetness. It is the seat of your emotions—and when you are blocked here, it can manifest as blocks to your creativity or a range of other emotions in your life.

Take some time to feel the waves inside your hips, the currents in your pelvis. We are beings of water—sixty percent of our body is composed of it. Float on the ocean inside you. Sink into your watery depths. Feel the flowing motion inside and allow yourself to be carried by the waves.

As you unleash what has been frozen inside you, feel your inner-self liquify. Feel yourself become changeable, fluid, pliable. Feel yourself thaw. Connect with your life-force, that energy that first made you when your parents consummated their connection. Feel the water that surrounded you from the time before you were even born, the amniotic fluid in the womb. We are creatures of water—and when we can surrender to that elemental state, we find freedom.

Feel your sexuality and gender expression flowing in whatever designs it is meant to follow. Allow yourself to be exactly as you are—exactly as you were meant to be—and know that it's enough. Know that you are perfect just as you are. There's no one you need to impress, no one from whom you need to gain approval. Allow yourself to find acceptance with whatever you discover inside. You are beautiful and free.

Dwell in this space for several moments. Silently repeat to yourself the word "thaw." Invite everything to relax and flow.

> *"If you experience one traumatic event, you have the kind of PTSD that can be resolved in four to six months of therapy. But if you experience years and years of small stressors — little things where you think, 'Was that because of my sexuality?' — that can be even worse."*
> **—William Elder, sexual trauma researcher**

Growing up queer is traumatic. A queer person will always feel different, even on a subtle level. The amount of stress that comes from this experience can be frustrating at its best—and deadly at its worst. As much as I wish I could say that the LGBTQ+ community has done a good job (as a whole) healing their past hurts, examining why they feel dissatisfied, and seeking wholeness—this is not the case. Many of the queer people I know struggle with addiction, self-abuse, spousal abuse, and suicidal tendencies.

Unlike other minority communities, queer people don't necessarily grow up in families that share their culture. Even in an open and affirming environment, they will still likely feel different from their parents and siblings. With no one to empathize with or fully relate to them, they will be prone to high levels of psychological trauma that could take a lifetime to resolve.

This is why drug use is rampant in the gay community. Men hop themselves up on methamphetamines so they can plow through three sleepless days on a high of horniness and unflagging stamina. They inflate themselves with steroids, so they can compensate for the scared, vulnerable boys inside. They engage in verbally and emotionally abusive behavior with their partners, with themselves, and with people they love. As much as I love my rainbow brothers—we all have so much work to do in order to come into wholeness.

One would think that the queer community would turn to one another for solace and healing, but this is often not the case. The trauma we have endured often makes us lash out at others. We harass innocent others for being unattractive, overweight, lacking a hyper-sexualized presentation of gender. Often, it is the insufficiencies that one perceives in one's self that get turned outward and hurled at hapless others.

There is an epidemic of un-acceptance. Just because someone is out and open about their identity doesn't mean that they have done the necessary work to establish self-love, healing, and the overcoming of shame. Too many people use sex, chemicals, or self-harm to quell the anxiety they feel inside. Too many young queer people *still* commit suicide—their numbers are three times higher than their heteronormative peers, even with as much of a shift toward acceptance as we've seen in America.[5]

Until every faction of the queer community can come to genuinely celebrate all the stripes in the rainbow flag—to firmly accept that the feminine is just as valuable as masculine, that gender-atypicality is just as beautiful as typicality, that the celibate is just as radical as polyamorous—we will continue to suffer. Each of us must diligently work within ourselves to celebrate what makes us unique, and then, in return, offer each person a welcoming embrace regarding their own differences. We are all queer—and there is no right or wrong way to enact queerness, to present identity.

We as humans must affirm that every life has value. Until we can see that we are all perfect in our oddities and our uniqueness, we will continue to hurt ourselves and one another. The great news is, once you develop compassion and acceptance for yourself—it becomes much easier to extend that grace to others.

So offer kindness, bless your neighbors, and promote diversity. We are all beautiful, swirling rainbows. It's time to celebrate yourself in your radiant, complex entirety.

"To love oneself is the beginning of a lifelong romance."
— **Oscar Wilde, writer and gay provocateur**

I want you to go through your whole day repeating the following phrase:

I am enough. I am enough. Just as I am, I am enough.

What would happen if you truly, fully took this to heart? That you, just as you are right now, are perfect? What if you gave yourself permission to simply be. You *are* enough, I promise. Now, you've got to teach yourself to believe it.

You are worthy of love and acceptance because you exist. Every person is worthy of feeling beautiful, radiant, and whole. You don't have to do, prove, or earn anything to demonstrate your worthiness. You are perfect and complete just as you are.

A tree does not require your permission to grow new leaves in the springtime, to reach up for the sky, to grow wider. A flower doesn't need your blessing in order to unfurl its petals, to release its intoxicating perfume, or to call to the honeybees for pollination. Why are you waiting for someone else's arbitrary approval to allow yourself to unfold into all your glory? Why are you thinking that you must only exist in one particular (and often, narrow-minded) way? Why can't you just allow yourself to bloom in whatever way that you were meant to? Why are you so concerned with others' opinions or censure?

You are wild. You are untamed. You were meant to be someone very specific. Why hold back your innate talents? Shine forth and allow the world to marvel at your beauty. Only by being enthusiastically you will you be able to connect with your ecstatic self. You need to find wholeness in order for your luminosity to fully ignite.

I encourage you to do whatever you need in order to heal your old wounds, let go of your old hurts, and bring your full self to the forefront. Be bold. Be enthusiastically you. You are worthy of love and acceptance—and the first person you need to get approval from is yourself. You are deserving. You are wonderful. You are prismatically, beautifully queer.

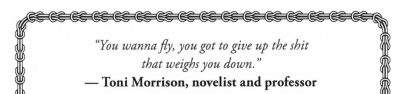

"You wanna fly, you got to give up the shit that weighs you down."
— **Toni Morrison, novelist and professor**

SUMMARY:

— **Gender/Sex/Sexuality are all different, and there are count less combinations between the spectrums.**

— **Examine moments from your own life where perhaps you were different than you always supposed yourself to be.**

— **All forms of queerness are beautiful and valid. Learn to ac cept and love yourself for wherever you are—in whatever ways you exist in the rainbow.**

Chapter 5 $7/_8$^{ths}:

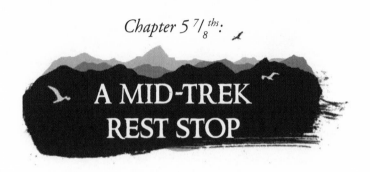

A MID-TREK REST STOP

*"I knew who I was this morning, but I've changed
a few times since then."*
—Lewis Carroll, *Alice in Wonderland*

L et's pause here for a moment for a mid-book check-in.

At this point, you might be thinking, "What the hell did I get myself into?" You probably thought this book was going to be about self-care, bubble baths, consuming copious amounts of chocolate, positive affirmations, hugging kittens, and riding your imaginary unicorn into the land of abundance where you'd sit under a Bodhi tree with Morgan Freeman and learn all the mysteries of the universe.

My apologies.

Self-exploration is a messy business and, if you are using this book properly, you've probably had at least one minor freak out thus far? Or—oh—a major one?

When we confront the barriers that are holding us back from our truest selves—when we deconstruct the walls that have formed the towers of our lives—it is normal and healthy for the mind to respond by resisting. Maybe you put this book on a shelf—or in the trash. Perhaps you went and wept into your pillow. Maybe you've screamed, "This author is an idiot! What does he know? I'm no queer person with a hidden shadow-side."

Whatever you are experiencing—it's okay. It's normal. Just like massaging a muscle that's been knotted up for some time, there's going to be discomfort as you dig into it. You are going to feel discomfort as you dismantle your long-held assumptions. Keep breathing—keep working on letting your fear dissolve.

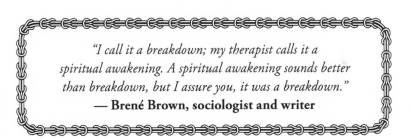

> *"I call it a breakdown; my therapist calls it a spiritual awakening. A spiritual awakening sounds better than breakdown, but I assure you, it was a breakdown."*
> — **Brené Brown, sociologist and writer**

MEDITATION VII

Close your eyes and focus on whatever you're feeling inside. Any emotions—pain, anxiety, sadness, joy, grief, longing. It doesn't matter what's there. Just observe whatever it is without judgment.

Calmly check in with your emotions for a few moments.

Once you find a place of calm, an ability to be present to your feelings without judgment—silently repeat to yourself one or a few of the following phrases:

Whatever I am feeling is okay.

Whatever I am experiencing is perfect.

136

I am alright as I am.
Whatever I am thinking is fine.

We can too easily become critical of ourselves and our experiences. We can chastise ourselves for not handling things better, for not being stronger, for not being kinder to ourselves. Let it be okay to be wherever you are. Allow yourself to exist without critiquing your behavior. You are so much more than whatever thoughts are going through your mind. You are so much more than the emotions you are feeling. You are a deep well of a greater force.

After all, if you can watch your thoughts occurring, if you can observe your emotions—that means that your thoughts and feelings cannot be who you quintessentially are deep down. If there is any separation between you and what you're watching—that means that the object of your observation cannot be you. Your mind might be experiencing emotions, but those emotions aren't you. Your mind might be a waterfall of cascading thoughts, but those thoughts are also not you. You are something so much greater—cosmic, timeless, infinite.

See if you can watch the comings and goings of your mind and emotions without identifying any of them as "being you." See if you can watch the experience of discomfort happen, without judging yourself.

Whatever you are feeling is perfect.
Whatever is happening is alright.
You are enough, just as you are.
You do not need to do anything—allow yourself to simply be.
You are already whole, beautiful, and complete.

Trust that everything will be okay. You are okay. You are safe.

Take as much time as you need to find your center and relax into this knowledge.

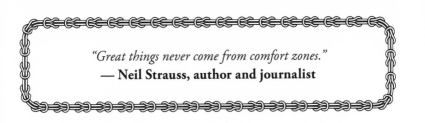

We are all going to feel pain from time to time. It is an inherent fact of living. But what we do with our response to that pain—that is our choice. We can learn to see pain as a teacher, as an opportunity to move more gracefully through the discomfort. Or, we can see pain as a burden, something to avidly and vehemently avoid.

One of the greatest tools for living gracefully is to acknowledge that we are going to hurt. We do not get to opt out of pain. What we can select, however, is whether or not we want to suffer. We can experience the sensations of discomfort—but not be consumed by it. Yes, sometimes things happen to us that feel devastating. Yes, we experience injury beyond what seems fair or just. But our response to that stimulus is our choice to make.

Furthermore, the pain we feel is our brain alerting us to a perceived threat to our continued survival. We can opt to dwell on its observations or put our focus elsewhere. In Norman Doidge's book, *The Brain's Way of Healing*, he shares a story about a time when he horrendously broke his leg in several places. It was a brutal accident—but so long as he stayed perfectly still and waited for the paramedics, his leg felt more or less fine. It was when he tried to move that the pain receptors would fire, urging him to pay attention to the damage. It was his brain's way of saying, "Stop it! Stay right there. If you move, you'll put us at greater risk."

He goes on to explain how he instructed the EMTs to dose him with unusually high levels of painkillers so his brain wouldn't get stuck in a pain feedback loop. He needed his brain to focus elsewhere, because it could easily get overly honed-in on the suffering—and that hyper focused awareness of pain could become chronic. He was aware that he was indeed injured—but he opted to redirect his awareness somewhere other than on the suffering, which ultimately allowed him to heal faster.

We ought to be similarly careful of where we focus our mental energy. Yes, we may be hurting for a good reason—but do we need to put all of our consciousness toward the discomfort? Would it be possible to instead say, "Yes, this hurts. Yes, this stinks. But I am going to focus on my breath. I am going to focus on all the many blessings and good qualities of what is going on in this moment. I don't need to be dragged down by the discomfort."

This may just seem like sunny optimism—but you know, what? It works. In Jim Collin's book, *Good to Great*, he shared what is now widely known as the "Stockdale Paradox." He interprets the story of vice-presidential candidate, naval officer, and Vietnam prisoner of war, James Stockdale—a man who survived horrendous torture during his seven years as a hostage. Stockdale recounts that it wasn't the realists that survived the internment camp—nor was it the sunny optimists who kept giving themselves arbitrary deadlines when they assured themselves they'd be rescued. Instead, it was the ones with quiet reliance, who *knew* with certainty that they would eventually prevail, but didn't set specific guidelines, deadlines, or expectations as to how or when that would happen.

So, too, can we adopt a similar vantage of things with ourselves, "The specifics don't matter. I know that I am going to be okay. I am going to be able to endure any hardship. I don't need to focus on the minutia of the pain. I am going to send my focus onward toward the ultimate goal—being okay. I am not going to let suffering define me."

> *"I want to know if you can sit with pain, mine or your own, without moving to hide it, or fade it, or fix it."*
> **— Oriah Mountain Dreamer's poem, The Invitation**

Building on what we explored in the previous meditation—find a comfortable seat and breathe into the space of discomfort you feel inside. That discomfort might be emotional—your sense of selfhood and identity being challenged. It might be physical—a knot in your gut. It might be mental.

Take several breaths to just feel out the pain. Where does it exist, precisely? Where are its edges? How deep does it run?

Try, as best you can, to let go of any qualitative language around what you're feeling. Let go of words like "good" or "bad" or "intense" or "mild" or even "new" or "old." Let your pain be whatever it is, without needing to label it, fix it, or define it.

Then, I want you to breathe into the source of your sorrow. Imagine your inhale as being a warm, soothing balm. Like herbal tea pouring over jagged ice, feel the epicenter of your pain melting. Feel it calmed. Don't necessarily try to get rid of it—just let it mellow. Allow yourself to become comfortable with the discomfort inside. Find peace with it. Let it exist—but kindly let it know that it doesn't need to keep hollering at you—claiming all your attention.

Observe how you and your suffering are not the same thing—you are separate. Pain might be an experience you are having—but it is not who you are. Treat it like a houseguest—let it sit where it wants, be attentive to it, but do not try to think of it as being yourself. It is just a visitor taking up residence for a while. Listen to the story it has to tell you—but don't get too caught up in its narrative. Listen without judgment—listen without overly investing. Be curious—but don't succumb to the story of which it's trying to convince you.

As you sit with pain, sense inside yourself that you are still whole, beautiful, radiant, and perfect. No amount of suffering will ever change that. You are well, just as you are, despite any limitations you presently feel. You are indelible, perfect, and complete. Nothing will ever diminish the reality of you.

Sit with your experience of pain—and once you've learned what it has to teach you—come back to your body and let everything you observed wash away. Come back and be well.

> "Pain is inevitable. Suffering is optional. Say you're running and you think, 'Man, this hurts, I can't take it anymore.' The 'hurt' part is an unavoidable reality, but whether or not you can stand anymore is up to the runner himself."
> — Haruki Murakami, Japanese writer

It's important to remember that coming into wholeness is more akin to a cross-country hike than a quarter-mile sprint. Finding a sense of lasting belonging is a process of unfolding, a peeling back of layer after layer to connect with our true selves. This journey will take time—months and years of work, rather than hours. A weekend retreat can spark a lifetime of self-discovery, but it isn't the entirety of the experience in and of itself.

If you find that you need to take a break and come back to this book—that's completely alright. Do not rush this journey—it will take whatever time it takes. You cannot go to the gym and expect to bicep curl fifty-pound dumbbells in your first week. Nor should you expect to come into true self-understanding in a similarly brief amount of time. It took decades to become the person you are today—and while a conscious and purposeful process will expedite the deconstruction process—it still takes considerable time to build replacement neural pathways, to settle into an altered state of awareness. Allow your trek to unfold at the right time, in the right way, and trust that all will click into place when you are ready. There is no need to rush.

"Above all, trust in the slow work of God. We are quite naturally impatient in everything to reach the end without delay. We should like to skip the intermediate stages. We are impatient of being on the way to something unknown, something new. And yet it is the law of all progress that it is made by passing through some stages of instability—and that it may take a very long time.

And so I think it is with you; your ideas mature gradually—let them grow, let them shape themselves, without undue haste. Don't try to force them on, as though you could be today what time (that is to say, grace and circumstances acting on your own goodwill) will make of you tomorrow."

**—Pierre Teilhard de Chardin,
French philosopher and Jesuit priest**

EXERCISE

Use the space below to journal about whatever you are experiencing at this point in your adventure toward selfhood. Use kind and soft language to describe yourself and your process.

_____

_____

_____

_____

Go to your music library and find at least one song that represents whatever you are feeling right now—or create a playlist of a few songs that seem to pull on you in some way. Then, turn up your speakers, shut the door to whatever room you are in, and exuberantly dance out your feelings. Be willing to look ridiculous.

Many of the emotion-processing centers of our brains are pre-verbal; they are older sections, evolutionarily speaking, that do not connect to the language-articulate sections of our minds. Expressing yourself through physical movement can be a great way to tap into these deeper brain areas and gain better self-awareness.

Allow yourself to move freely—surrender all inhibitions. Dance like no one's watching—and discover how your body will speak to you through ecstatic gestures.

Song Title: _____ by: _____
_____

Song Title: _____ by: _____
_____

Song Title: _____ by: _____
_____

Song Title: _____ by: _____
_____

Song Title: _____ by: _____
_____

If any song lyrics keep jumping out to you, pulling your focus, write them down below. They might articulate—in more poetic language—what you are experiencing. This is part of the reason why we turn to music to soothe our souls—artists put into words notions that we cannot ourselves name. Emotions are like fluttering butterflies—

they are difficult to catch with outstretched fingers. We require the subtly of a net.

Lyrics that speak to me:

_____

_____

_____

_____

_____

_____

_____

_____

_____

_____

_____

_____

_____

_____

_____

_____

_____

_____

_____

_____

_____

When you are ready, continue on. Take a rest stop if you need. And, indeed, if it takes you a while until you are ready to hit the trail again, that's quite alright. Allow yourself time to process whatever it is that you are currently going through. The next chapter will be waiting for you whenever you are finally ready to reengage.

There is no sliding backward. Growth happens in spirals. When you're ready to start again—you will know that you are ready. Do not rush the process. You cannot lose any genuine revelations that you've gained—that learning is yours to keep. Allow the process to unfurl in the beautiful way it needs. At your own pace. In your own rhythm.

SUMMARY:

— **You are not your thoughts, emotions, or the suffering you might presently feel.**

— **Healing takes time; do not rush the journey toward wholeness.**

Chapter 6:

GRAB YOUR CLIMBING BUDDY'S HAND

"Set your life on fire. Seek those who fan your flames."
— Rumi, Sufi poet and mystic

W e've been spending quite a bit of time exploring who we might be, what we fear, and how we might be different than we originally supposed. I think that it's time now to leave the house, turn off our devices, and test our observations in the context of the real world.

Only so much self-learning can happen in isolation. We can create theories regarding our identities, who we believe ourselves to be—but until they are actively explored amongst other humans, they remain just that: theories. We need to test our mettle, experiment, and learn through failure. Implementing our new self-awareness in the context of social interactions can be a great way to fuel further growth.

Furthermore, each person in our lives can serve as a teacher. They can represent qualities we wish to grow toward—or, frankly, away from. They can remind us of our better angles or highlight qualities

147

that we'd be better off avoiding. Regardless of their perceived positivity or negativity, we can learn a great deal from everyone who is currently in our lives.

Our relationships can reveal a great deal about ourselves, too. Who are the sorts of persons we feel drawn to? What are their priorities? How do they choose to spend their time and energy? Are they kind, selfless, and forthright? Are they often selfish or petty? Do they demonstrate a strong connection to their inner worth, truth, and brilliance? If an objective observer were watching us mingling together, would we appear to be the sort of people with whom I would be proud to be associated?

These are all excellent questions to ask of ourselves. Earlier in the book, I brought up the notion of resonance and vibration. I explained how we attract others who are resonating at a similar frequency as ourselves—something within us calls to one another. It was true for my secretly queer friends and me in high school—and it is also true of every social relationship I maintain. There's something about our vibrations that pull us toward one another. By studying what in another person calls to me, I can better understand aspects of myself. Try to notice what about the people with whom you regularly connect magnetizes you.

Each relationship we maintain—even very casual ones, like a gym buddy or an acquaintance that you see seldom—can teach us something. Each person with whom we interact can be an active representation of the man/woman/fluid person we wish to be. Each soul can be our teacher, guide, or mentor—if we are open to learning from them and what they represent. Also, it is important that we spend time in people's physical presence—digital interactions can only take us so far. Having more face-to-face time is precisely what this chapter is going to encourage you to seek out.

In-person interactions matter a great deal. Numerous studies are now linking increased time spent in front of screens with decreased quality of life.[1] Elevated consumption of social media, in particular, is one of the worst instigators for reduced wellbeing. Researchers believe that anxiety and depression are now running rampant through the teenage community—in numbers previously unseen—because of the ever-present, intoxicating glow of apps.[1]

Further, social media's newsfeeds foster increased levels of personal distress because people's postings do not accurately represent reality. We see friends' lives in highlighted bursts—bright triumphs, meticulously arranged selfies, impeccably clean living rooms—and our own lives feel inadequate by comparison. No one's existence is filtered or edited day-to-day—but most people's online presence makes it seem like each day really is that rosy and glossy. Social media makes us feel unpolished, imperfect, and deficient. For adolescents, recognizing the difference between curated representation and reality is nearly impossible due to their brain development—but adults, too, fall for the fantasy of believing others' online lives are their truth.

We get tricked into seeing influencers' expertly staged living rooms and thinking that their homes are always that tidy and neatly arranged. Our eyes go wide at their impossible abs but fail to recognize that they are in really good lighting and at the end of a six-week fast. We see them as a smiling couple holding their new baby but miss the chronic late nights, early mornings, and sleep deprivation that has been wearing them down. When we interact with other souls in an online format, we only see the parts of them that they wish to display. It is an incomplete picture—and one that inevitably makes us feel inadequate.

For we are keenly aware of our own messy bits. We see the left-over pizza on the counter from three nights ago, the closet overflowing with useless junk, the cellulite and backrolls. We know that we are not perfect. But, try as we might, we fall prey to the notion that somehow, somewhere, there are luminous human beings who have their shit entirely together. This is simply not true. We are all messy—all struggling. It's unfair to frustrate ourselves with the perception that others have it all figured out. No one does.

> *"The reason we struggle with insecurity is because we compare our behind-the-scenes with everyone else's highlight reel."*
> — **Steven Furtick, pastor and writer**

It is also too easy to believe that cyber connections are suitable replacements for face-to-face relationships. They are not. The benefit of spending quality time in proximity to another living, breathing person cannot be overstated. When we smell each other's cologne, hear the shifting of each other's joints, feel the pulse within each other's fingertips—these cues stimulate neural pathways in our brains. These tangible experiences enact chemical reactions that allow us to better understand ourselves and our place in the world in a way that digital formats cannot recreate.

Johann Hari, author of the book *Lost Connections,* says, "The Internet was born into a world where many people had already lost their sense of connection to each other. [...] The web arrived offering them a kind of parody of what they were losing—Facebook friends in place of neighbors, video games in place of meaningful work, status updates in place of status in the world." The approximation of life that we find online is akin to a junk food binge: it fills us up, but it doesn't leave us nourished as a substantial meal would. It's a surrogate for real life—but not a complete one. It lacks the nuance and depth of fleshy relationships. Or, as Johann Hari goes on to say, "[Interacting with people online] is a bit like the difference between pornography and sex: it addresses a basic itch, but it's never satisfying."

When we spend in-person time with people who genuinely engage us—where there's a free exchange of ideas, passion, and interest—we grow. While there can be times when you feel notably changed and improved through virtual communications, what are the most memorable interactions you recall from your past? You probably envision laughing with a friend beside a bonfire, or a late-night tête-à-tête whispered under bed covers. When we think of the most impactful moments of learning from one another—they are usually accompanied by the sweat and sweetness of face-to-face interactions.

Ask yourself, "How many people do I have in my life that I would love to have dinner with—that, through our conversations, I would learn something new about the world and myself? How many friends do I have where the exchange between us would elevate my day-to-day existence?" Hopefully, you have at least one person who comes to mind when answering these questions—we need mutually meaningful relationships to thrive. But if no one came to mind, you are not alone. A poll by YouGov shows that twenty-seven percent of millennials say that they have no close friends.[2]

Think about that statistic for a second—one in four millennials say that they have no one in whom they can confide when tragedy strikes, no one to celebrate with when they make a major career breakthrough. When they achieve a milestone or grieve a loss, they have no one to ring up. Even a rich and successful millennial like Taylor Swift admits to feeling the epidemic of loneliness in her generation. In her documentary, *Miss Americana*, she comments that when she swept the Grammy Awards for her album, *1989*, she felt so alone. She says, "You get to the mountaintop and you look around, and you're like, *Oh, God—what now?* I didn't have a partner that I climbed it with that I could, like, high-five. I didn't have anyone I could talk to who could relate to what I was...what I...you know? I had my mom, but, I just wondered, shouldn't I have someone that I could call right now?"

Let's add onto this awareness a 2009 laboratory study performed by the University of Chicago on cancer in rats.[3] They revealed that "rats living in isolation experienced a 135 percent increase in the number of tumors and a more than 8,000 percent increase in [tumor] size" for rats already predisposed to mammary gland growths. If you are lonely, it will be difficult to truly thrive. Isolation kills—and online connections are not sufficient replacements for in-person relationships.

While it can be challenging to maintain meaningful relationships with others—especially as we get older and the social mixing that comes with school and new working environments diminishes—it is entirely necessary to create new social bonds for our health, happiness, and growth. Finding a tribe, a few people with whom we resonate, can be one of the best ways for us to be healthy and to know ourselves better. Other people can provide signposts that direct us toward our most authentic selves.

When we feel a kinship with another person, there are parts of ourselves that resonate in harmony with them. If you are attracted to spending time with visual artists, for example, it might reveal that you have latent artistic talents or abilities that have thus far remained unexpressed. If you find yourself drawn to people who are working recovery programs, it could highlight your own desire for personal evolution. When something about a person pulls you toward them, it can indicate a part of your consciousness that is being highlighted. By spending time in the presence of people with whom you resonate, you can better know your essence.

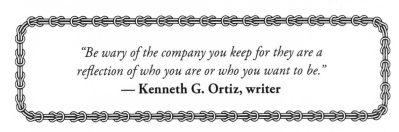

"Be wary of the company you keep for they are a reflection of who you are or who you want to be."
— **Kenneth G. Ortiz, writer**

The first time I consciously became aware of resonating with another person occurred during my senior year of college. I had encountered a fellow student who had just returned from studying abroad. He had spent six months in a Buddhist monastery in India, four months in sub-Saharan Africa researching indigenous dance styles, and three months volunteering at a camp for disabled children in Indonesia. He was spiritual, wildly authentic, and unapologetically queer. While I might not have had much clarity regarding my own sexual identity at that time—I felt pulled to him. There was a quality about his presence that spoke to my spirit, and I desperately wanted to know more. I craved spending time with him in a way I couldn't recall feeling with anyone prior—he represented so much about who I unconsciously knew myself to be.

He was admittedly eccentric. He would set up a foot-washing station in the student commons and scrub passersby's feet while questioning them about their day and burning incense over an open flame. He would sit in the grass, strumming his guitar, and crooning songs about cosmic love and world peace. He refused to spend money on anything that wasn't a vital necessity—he kept no furniture in his apartment apart from a mattress on the floor. He was well-traveled, a great listener, and immensely kind.

I remember thinking that it was interesting that we would go somewhere and people would often ask if we were brothers. Sure, there was an amount of physical resemblance between us—but more so, I believe that people were picking up on the energetic resonance between us. We were birds chirping the same melody—except he had much more developed vocal cords than I. He represented a well-adjusted iteration of my potential—he was already rooted into his self.

This young man was open about his sexuality. He had a boyfriend, and they lived together. Even though I would have been mortified to imagine myself in a same-sex relationship—I somehow carved out an exemption for him and acknowledged a spark of sexual attraction. The openness inside of him allowed me to feel longings that were bound down with leather straps and iron locks. Indeed, it would be another five years before I would again permit myself to imagine intimacy with another man.

Given how inspired I felt from my time around him, it's not surprising that I moved into an ashram shortly after graduating college. I followed a roadmap that he had set—the ashram I picked was not too different from the monastery that he had chosen in India. By making him part of my tribe, I better came to understand myself and my truth. He taught me.

If I had never met him, I would not have found such a keen understanding. Being with him allowed me to recognize the reverberations inside of me that had been previously kept mute. Although we lost touch after school ended—he had no cellphone and wasn't on social media—I thought on him with gratitude for years to come.

It is important to point out that this loving, carefree, queer identity was in direct opposition to the persona I was actively trying to cultivate—the swaggering, heteronormative, career-driven film actor. While much of me was still bent on achieving what I thought would bring me the greatest happiness (movie stardom), a wiggling part of my mind began to chomp away at that delusion. The months of interacting with him fostered the hairline cracks in my persona that would spread to become fissures and gullies. Cracks that would one day break open and permit me to recognize my real self. By being in physical proximity, the cells in my body got to feel his particular vibration. If I had only seen his online posts, I would not have gotten as clear of a chemical understanding of him.

Interestingly enough, the next time I would encounter someone with whom I would feel such immense and immediate kinship—who possessed an essence that felt so intrinsically attuned with my own—ended up being the man that became my husband.

"It's better to hang out with people better than you. Pick out associates whose behavior is better than yours and you'll drift in that direction."
—Warren Buffet, investor extraordinaire and philanthropist

Come up with the names of the people with whom you spend the most face-to-face time. Next to their names—please write what you admire most about that person or what you gain from their company.

Name   What's nourishing about them/our interactions

_____   _____
_____   _____
_____   _____
_____   _____
_____   _____
_____   _____
_____   _____
_____   _____
_____   _____
_____   _____
_____   _____
_____   _____
_____   _____
_____   _____
_____   _____
_____   _____
_____   _____
_____   _____
_____   _____

Looking over the list of people you came up with, were there any for whom it was a struggle to name a positive attribute in how they enrich your life? If so, it may be a sign that you have outgrown that relationship—which is not a bad thing. As we develop as humans, we may need different types of relationships, different people around us.

For this next list, please come up with people you admire or who you would like to get to know better. These may be acquaintances or friends that have been distant for some time. Try to articulate what precisely draws you to them.

Name	What's nourishing about them/our interactions

Notice the qualities you came up with. It's okay if some of them are superficial—but, hopefully, not all of your reasons are just "they're really cute." We want to dig—reach into the core of people's beings and find what about them calls to our spirits.

For this last list, please dream up people who you aspire to interact with, but maybe never will. Perhaps they're celebrities or have already passed on—come up with some archetypal role-models who inspire you. My personal list might include Nelson Mandela, Mother Teresa, Martin Luther King Jr., Jane Goodall, or Mohandas Gandhi.

Name	What's nourishing about them/our interactions

Go back to the previous exercise and take a gander at the second list you generated—the people with whom you would like to cultivate a stronger relationship. Pick one to three of the names and write out a message that you could send, inviting them for coffee, tea, or an adult beverage. It might sound something like this:

> *Hi, _____. I hope this finds you well! I know we haven't chatted in a while—but you've been coming to mind recently. I so appreciate you, what you do, and think it would be great to catch up. While I know that you're very busy—would you be available for coffee in the next two weeks? I would love to hear how things are going. Warmly, _____.*

Pay attention to some of the key points that make this sample message work. It is about the recipient and wanting to know how they're doing (people usually like talking about themselves), it's low-pressure (I don't sound like I'm desperate), and I offer a specific activity and a time frame to do it within (if you just say "sometime," it doesn't create a window by which the person needs to respond). You can copy and paste my message, but I would encourage you to pen your own.

A message for potential new friends (or rekindling current/old friendships):

_____

_____

_____

_____

_____

_____

_____

Send it through whichever medium you feel is best: text, email, greeting card, phone call, carrier pigeon, etc. As filmmaker Woody Allen reminds us, "Eighty percent of success is just showing up." While you may get rejected, most people will be flattered that you thought of them. And, as a friend of mine once reminded me, "you are guaranteed a one-hundred-percent failure rate if you don't even try." Act boldly by putting yourself out there. When you have your meet-and-greet date set, jot it down in the space below:

I am meeting _____ to do _____ at this date/time: _____

I am meeting _____ to do _____ at this date/time: _____

I am meeting _____ to do _____ at this date/time: _____

"It is an absolute human certainty that no one can know his own beauty or perceive a sense of his own worth until it has been reflected back to him in the mirror of another loving, caring human being."
— **John Joseph Powell, Jesuit priest and writer**

Another aspect of face-to-face interactions that is impossible to replicate through a computer screen is touch. Whether through a friend holding our hand or mom's affectionate hug, we need physical stimulation to our skin. When was the last time someone held you while in a social setting? Perhaps a quick slap-on-the-back-style hug while saying hello or goodbye?

Americans have adopted a culture of non-touch, especially amongst men. Men don't hold hands, don't play with each other's hair, don't caress one another's faces, or sit on each other's laps. There is a dearth of physical connection amongst all Americans, but particularly those who are male-identified. Researcher Sidney Jourard did a study in the 1960s where he counted how many times companions sitting at a café would reach out and conversationally touch each other. When doing his observations in France and Puerto Rico, he observed that they would touch each other one-hundred and ten times and one-hundred and eighty times, respectively. In the United States and Great Britain, by comparison, dining companions would only reach out for touch twice and zero times, again respectively.[4] This lack of physical connection is keeping us lonely and emotionally distant from one another—and also from our own selves.

Allowing yourself to be the recipient of platonic touch provides both psychological and physiological benefits. Researchers Darlene Francis and Michael Meaney found that rats with mothers that groomed them regularly as infants grew up to be calmer, more resilient to stress, and possessed measurably heartier immune systems.[5] Studying humans, Tiffany Field observed that prenatal newborns that were held for fifteen-minute increments, three times per day, gained forty-seven percent more weight than the premature infants receiving standard medical protocol during their first week of life.[5] Touch brings us into our bodies and strengthens our connection to life.

When I was younger, I feared touch. I would keep my limbs to myself and shrink back—as if I were undeserving—when someone approached me with a hug. I remember watching my peers put their arms around one another or lean into each other—and, while it seemed appealing, I felt unworthy to partake. I sensed that I was dangerous, unlovable. My buried fears regarding my sexual identity made me wonder if someone touching my skin would be able to feel the tissue-paper-like façade I had constructed. I was a piñata-man: cardboard skin hiding a hollow interior. I didn't want them to realize that I was fake.

It took until my mid-twenties for me to start exploring physical forms of affection—even platonically. Touch initially felt forbidden and strange. Over time, however, it eventually became a healing salve for me. I soaked in the physical gestures of kindness like a dry sponge, letting the sensations soothe decades of self-loathing and feelings of insufficiency. A tight embrace, a pat on the arm, a squeeze of a hand taught me that I was worthy, that I was seen, and that I was valued. Touch helped to reconnect me with my body.

> "Nothing in this world compares to the comfort and security of having someone just hold your hand."
> **—Richelle E. Goodrich, author**

It is important to mention that for face-to-face connection to provide a lasting benefit, both parties have to feel like they gain something from the experience. Studies show that transactional interactions—like paying a massage therapist, fitness coach, psychological therapist, or sex-worker for their skills—don't stimulate the same neural pathways as when everyone involved believes that they've benefited.[6] That's not to say that one-way relationships don't have value (I have certainly enjoyed many wonderful massage-therapy sessions), it's just that we need to cultivate relationships that work both ways. We need to feel like we are improving someone else's life through our connection, not just our own. We are hardwired for altruism. When relationships are entirely one-sided, it will leave us feeling less validated.

Find a way to receive touch—and, ideally, offer it in return. The most available and lowest emotional-risk form of experiencing physical touch is to hire a professional. Go to a spa and pay for an hour massage session; attend a yoga class and ask the instructor for physical adjustments; book a session with a professional cuddler (yes, that's really a thing). This can be a great way to start acclimating your body to accept affection from others. If you can allow others to nourish you—you may be better able to care for yourself.

A more vulnerable—but ultimately more rewarding—way to experience touch is by sharing it with someone for whom you care. Invite a few people over for a platonic cuddle party, ask a friend for a long hug, offer to hold a companion's hand while walking together.

It is important to always establish enthusiastic consent when offering touch—unwanted or uninvited physical interaction is never appropriate. Unless someone responds by saying, "Heck, yeah!"—their agreement might not be wholehearted. Someone who sounds hesitant, unsure, or coerced is not offering true consent. A "yes" said with uncertainty is often a "no" or a "can we negotiate this further?" If a person doesn't seem excited by your suggestion, kindly redirect your query to someone else. Learn to hear "no" and not be offended—learn to thank them for respecting their own boundaries.

When you are done, journal about your experiences below.

My experiences with touch:

_____

_____

_____

_____

_____

_____

_____

According to psychologist Miriam Akhtar, "Tactile stimulation can trigger oxytocin, the love hormone. It also lowers cortisol levels, reducing anxiety and stress. Touch has been shown to alleviate depression, improve immune function, reduce pain, enhance attentiveness, decrease blood pressure and calm the heart rate. It speeds recovery times from illness and surgery, aids digestion and boosts survival rates of patients with complex diseases."[7]

The great news is that many of the benefits of touch experienced with another living being can be recreated by touching one's self. Ayurveda, the wellness tradition of India, uses self-massage as a principal healing modality. Ayurvedic doctors recommend starting the day by massaging warm oil across the entire body before showering. The stroking motions help to stimulate the parasympathetic nervous system and build a more robust mind-body connection.

When we experience a sensation of disconnection from our inner truth, it is often paired with a separation from our physical bodies. Many have lived the experience of feeling "trapped in their heads." To quote the author James Joyce, "Mr. Duffy lived a short distance from his body." When we are afraid of our inner brilliance, we disassociate from the flesh—we try to create a buffer between our "selves" and our physical mechanisms.

When I was younger and would go for a professional massage, I almost couldn't feel it when the therapist would start to work on any area below my diaphragm—I was that disassociated from my lower half. It was almost like the masseur's hands would vanish when they got down to my hips, knees, or feet. It took a long time for me to accept and welcome healing touch. As we permit physical interaction to enter our lives, we give ourselves permission to sink back into our skin. We start to inhabit the marvelous machines that we call bodies.

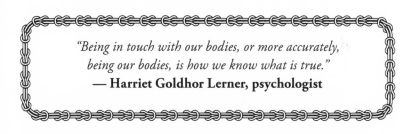

> *"Being in touch with our bodies, or more accurately, being our bodies, is how we know what is true."*
> — **Harriet Goldhor Lerner, psychologist**

EXERCISE

The practice of self-massage in Ayurveda is called *Abhyanga*. It should be done when you are not in a rush and have time to dedicate to being with yourself. Like any mindfulness-based activity, approach this with deliberate attention—bring your focus to your fingertips and whatever part of your body is currently under them.

Start by setting down an old towel on the floor of your bathroom—one that you won't mind getting oily. Fill a squeeze bottle or a small jar with oil and warm it by placing it in a bath of hot water. Traditionally, Ayurveda recommends using sesame or coconut oil for this practice.

Once the water is comfortably warm, place it beside your towel and sit down, fully naked. Starting with your extremities (toes, fingers, and crown of the head), gently rub the warm oil into your body. Notice how the temperature and texture help you to relax. Work in circular motions when you are passing over joints and long, sweeping strokes over stretches of bone. Move from the tips of your body toward your core, ending in the middle of your chest.

As you massage your body, silently tell yourself that you are beautiful. Thank your body for all the hard work it does, for it carrying you around everywhere you need to go. Regardless of what kind of body you have, be grateful for it. Express appreciation for each and every little part—the billions of neurons and muscle fibers and cells that have to coordinate to make mobility, respiration, and cognition possible. Stay present to the experience of being touched—notice the varied sensations.

Once you have completed your *Abhyanga* (which should take around fifteen minutes, if you're taking your time), sit on the towel in silence and meditate. Observe how your body, mind, and essence feel after several minutes of self-love. Notice how it feels to take time to truly nourish yourself.

When you're ready, step into a warm (but not hot) shower to wash off excess oil. Try not to scrub—you want to leave some of these beneficial oils in place. Soap only your hair and under your arms and groin. Once you're dry and dressed, make yourself a cup of tea and reflect on how you're changed by the experience.

In the space below, draw how your body felt before the self-message—and how it feels after. This does not need to be a literal depiction—you can just create arcs and lines that represent the energy of the practice.

Before my self-massage, my body felt like:

After my self-massage, my body now feels like:

The process of reconnecting with our bodies can unleash intense emotions because we store trauma in our physical forms. When you get scared—your shoulders tense. When you grieve—your core contracts. Your physical and emotional selves are inseparable. To reconnect with our true selves, we are going to have to press into the discomfort. Experiencing panic, anxiety, fear, or sorrow is to be expected when we yoke our awareness back to our physical forms. Like piercing a cyst, the toxic emotions will need to drain out. Try to pause, breathe, and observe the emotions arising with curiosity. Take your time and be kind to yourself. The process of cleansing can make you feel more pain en route to feeling better.

In this chapter, we have so far directed our attention to the topic of platonic touch and its benefits. As important as this type of touch is—erotic touch can be equally important. If you are having intense reactions to the work we've explored with embodiment thus far, this might be an excellent place to pause—take a break and settle into these previous exercises before moving on. On the other hand, if you are feeling comfortable with everything, please continue reading. Things are about to get a bit steamier.

Being a lover, feeling adored, allowing yourself to be thoroughly known by another human being can give us a profound understanding of ourselves and our worth. Our bodies are built for communion with another—and in that sacred space of an ecstatic breath, there can be an experience of wholeness. Spiritual traditions throughout history have paired the feeling of orgasm with the experience of knowing the divine. In fact, certain tantric yogic traditions describe the fourth state of awareness (besides dreaming, deep sleep, and wakefulness), called *Turiya*, as being the exact same state as we experience in the brief moments of an orgasmic high. Orgasm and enlightenment—possibly the exact same thing.

Allowing someone to lovingly, sensually touch you—and you offer it in return—can be some of the most meaningful and glorious experiences we have as humans. The act of being truly vulnerable with someone—allowing yourself to understand each facet of them and be known yourself—happens through sight, touch, scent, and taste—and through an unspeakable, energetic coupling. In that chemical, hormonal connection—we experience our own selves in the presence of another.

> *"I remember how it stopped seeming odd that in biblical Greek 'knowing' was used for making love. Whosit knew so-and-so. Carnal knowledge. It's what lovers trust each other with. Knowledge of each other, not of the flesh but through the flesh, knowledge of self, the real him, the real her, in extremis, the mask slipped from the face."*
> — **The Real Thing by Tom Stoppard, playwright**

The first time I was known, I was twenty-five. It was world-bending. To have someone that you care about—someone that you desire—see you, touch you, and appreciate you is a powerful intoxicant. Through a lover's eyes, I become better able to see myself. Years later,

I am now married—and I still get that awe-inspiring validation from my husband. Each morning, he looks at me anew—studies the contours of my face, drinks me in with concentration. His touch provides me with a profound knowing of my own worth. This person that I immensely respect sees me, likes what he sees, and affirms my value—both with his words and with his eyes. His touch heals old wounds and ignites my inner light to shine more brightly.

This is the power of romantic touch—to connect with another being and, through them, reconnect with ourselves. We are entirely whole on our own, but we can become so much more than our individualized self when sexual touch is approached with openness, compassion, passion, and vulnerability.

Notice the difference between what I am describing and—say—getting plastered and fucking in a bathroom stall. Not that anonymous sexual experiences can't be powerful and healing—I am sex-positive and think any situation can be meaningful when approached from the right vantage—but look at the difference in approach. Are you using someone purely as a sexual object to get off on, or are you striving for authentic connection? Are you willing to get truly vulnerable—by becoming both bodily naked and also emotionally exposed? We all crave intimacy—whether through touch or spirit—but so many of us keep blockades erected that prevent it.

Do you feel that while you may give someone access to your body, you refuse to let them access your mind or heart? A lot of people mistake sex for intimate interaction—and while the former can be fun, it ultimately doesn't provide lasting fulfillment. After a sexual (but non-intimate) encounter is over, most people feel reckless, ashamed, or longing for the next thrill. Many of those who seek physical intimacy but avoid vulnerability trail from one encounter to another like hungry ghosts—always eating but never satisfied.

It is possible to have a sexually fulfilling connection with another human being without removing a single article of clothing. Sensual touch does not need to mean fornication, though it certainly can be. The question is: does the experience you have with another being leave you and the other party(ies) more fulfilled, complete, and whole—

or diminished? Do you feel empowered, integrated, and deeply satisfied—or emptied? Do you feel shame around your actions—are they drawing you further away from your truth?

Too many people find that they can only experience sex while in a chemically altered state. Too many people use sex to distract themselves from their malaise, their boredom, or their dissatisfaction with life. Too many people use it to alleviate their feelings of powerlessness or abandonment. If you find yourself engaging in sexual encounters for any reasons like these—it might be time to take a step back and seek professional counseling. Sex should provide us experiences of being more connected, fuller, more loving, more integrated, or more kind.

Please don't get me wrong—I love that sex is being destigmatized in our culture. I am so appreciative that sex is a topic that can be openly talked about, that it is losing its taboo. Too many people have been taught to feel ashamed for their longings—and any time shame is present, a person cannot be healthy.

I've heard numerous stories about people finding empowerment by working as professional submissives, going to kink conferences, exploring their plushy fantasies. I have felt tremendous liberation by exploring the fringes of sexual expression—like the time my husband, a straight girlfriend of ours, and I wandered into the International Mister Leather in Chicago (a BDSM and kink convention). It was thrilling to see so many different types of men being unashamed of their bodies or their preferences—wandering through the booths and merchant stalls was affirming and beautiful for all three of us. An afternoon I spent at a bathhouse in the Marais district of Paris was one of the most beautiful and healing experiences of my life.

At the same time, I am concerned by how many people use sex to distance themselves from their essence, to try to fill a bottomless pit of dissatisfaction and longing. No number of hookups will make you feel good enough. No amount of unaware fucking will make you feel empowered.

Sex, when used well, can soothe the soul, provide self-knowledge, and give immense pleasure. It can help you recognize qualities that feel authentic to your truth. I hope that you have had the opportunity to feel the positive benefits of romantic touch—to communicate your needs and have them met by another being. I wish for you a wildly fulfilling sex life with a person or people who absolutely adore you. May you feel radiant, beautiful, and sexy as hell.

EXERCISE

You know where this exercise is going: find a way to explore sensual touch. It can be with another person—or it could even be with yourself. Try to be authentic and as emotionally vulnerable as you are able. Approach sensuality as a meditative act—being fully present to each embrace, each caress, each thrust. Try to remain aware not only of your own experience—but that of your partner(s). Listen to your body—lean into what feels good—and dare to be fully seen. Aim to gain a deeper understanding of yourself by being intimate with another. Be safe—get enthusiastic consent—and have fun. If you'd like, you can journal about your experiences below.

My sensual exploration impressions:

_____

_____

_____

_____

_____

_____

_____

_____

_____

_____

_____

_____

_____

_____

_____

_____

> "It's time we saw sex as the truly sacred art that it is.
> A deep meditation, a holy communion, and a dance with
> the force of creation."
> — **Marcus Allen, writer**

SUMMARY:

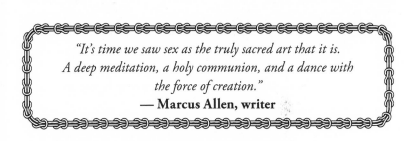

— We need time in the company of people who nourish our spirits—online interactions (by themselves) don't cut it.

— Physical touch makes us healthier, happier, and reconnected with our true selves.

— Whether romantic or platonic, we must approach intimacy with openness, vulnerability, and authenticity to make it meaningful.

Chapter 7:

SUN'S OUT, SHIRTS OFF

*"Women hide their imperfections instead
of accepting them as an added charm."*

— **Coco Chanel, fashion designer and entrepreneur**

I n the last chapter, I encouraged you to leave your house and
spend time in the company of loved ones. Maybe you went
out for dinner or drinks, maybe you scheduled a cuddle party,
perhaps you even got a little frisky—put on that navy number from
the back of your closet and painted the town crimson. If so—you go!
How did it feel?

If you are like most people, I imagine that the experience of having
your body in contact with another's brought up feelings of insecurity
and possibly even shame. So many of us experience discomfort when
it comes to showing or sharing our body with other people—most of
us have intense self-consciousness regarding our physiques and appearances.

In the modern world, we are barraged with advertising—and these
ads instill unrealistic body expectations. There are the scantily-clad

and anorexically-thin models on billboards, the chemically-chiseled actors on television with their impossible abs, and the artfully lounging influencers with their skin-tone buffed out in Photoshop. None of them reflect what humans actually look like.

My husband and I were traveling in Germany and wanted to experience some local culture. There, nudity is a social pastime—the Germans enjoy getting naked at beaches, in the woods, and at government-run bathing complexes. We were advised to patronize one of Munich's state-sponsored bathhouses—and when we arrived, we were greeted by fully-nude men and women lounging in saunas, sweating in steam rooms, and wading through thermal pools.

Neither he nor I had ever been in a coed nude environment. Seeing men and women socializing together in the buff was shocking in a few ways. First, the more obvious surprise was, being gay men, neither of us had spent much time around disrobed women. It was strange and foreign for us to see uncovered lady-parts. But the second and more remarkable takeaway was that we were seeing bodies that looked unaltered—as if they were the way that nature intended them.

In America, our bodies reflect our culture and social mores. We are a nation of excess, of consumerism. We do nothing half-heartedly—everything is either the "best" or the "worst." And this psychological tendency is reflected in people's physiques. At one end of the spectrum, we have people who struggle with obesity. According to the Center for Disease Control, nearly forty-three percent of Americans in 2018 are considered obese—and almost ten percent are morbidly obese.[1] On the other end of the spectrum, we have the fanatical fitness junkies—those who are unhealthfully pumped, plumped, injected, or sculpted.

Having scoped out the views at spas and locker rooms at home, I can report that it is rare to find someone who looks naturally fit, unaltered, and with an appropriate height to weight ratio. It is rare to see a body that reflects the way nature would have designed it to be with no artificial intervention.

At this spa in Germany, by contrast, there was hardly anyone who appeared overly worked-out, unnaturally thin, or notably overweight.

There were none with artificial tans, fake boobs, or obvious cosmetic procedures. No one seemed to be surgically-altered in the slightest—heck, only one person out of the dozens even had tattoos. There was a range of body types and shapes, but exceedingly few would have fallen into the category of obesity. It was such a consciousness-altering experience to see bodies that accurately reflected human potential—and it was a stark contrast to my domestic experiences.

Growing up, I was fascinated by fitness models. I thought their curves and bulges were beautiful and hypnotic. I would have given anything to look like them. When I was fourteen, my parents got me my first personal trainer. Despite how much effort I put in at the gym, I was dismayed to find that my body wasn't sculpting itself into the shapes I saw in glossy magazines.

It wasn't until my early thirties that I realized the extent to which steroids and growth hormones are utilized by the fitness and beauty industry. I was shocked to consult with individuals who made the study of this topic their life's work, to learn that almost everyone was using something to attain those physiques. We have developed a warped notion of what is natural and what is attainable. It's not what we think it is.

When was the last time that you encountered someone who appeared to take the middle-road regarding their appearance? So many individuals are obsessed with their bodies—they aren't thin-enough, young-enough, buff-enough. We exist in a culture where "wellness" and "fitness" personalities sell us products we don't need and prey on our insecurities—and meanwhile they're discreetly taking illegal supplements. I cannot name a single friend who hasn't dieted at some point, had cosmetic work done, or gone to some lengths to attain more "idealized" proportions. While working for greater health, wellbeing, and longevity are absolutely worthy goals and admirable—we have taken the pursuit of perfection to unhealthy extremes.

It is surprising that, for as much energy as we put into thinking about our bodies, America is a remarkably prudish culture. We no longer swim naked or even undress comfortably in front of our friends. I have watched countless men in locker rooms doing the "towel dance"—awkwardly shimmying out of their undergarments while wrapped in an undersized scrap of terry-cloth—so as never to be fully exposed. The absurdity of actively choosing to dress in such an uncomfortable manner highlights the immense shame we actually feel about our bodies and our selves.

Too many of us treat our physical forms as if they were disgraceful, something to hide or control. A dangerous force that must be protected and kept in check at all times. In order for us to supposedly feel body-positive, we are expected to attain unimaginable standards that do not reflect physiology. Men are not biologically meant to constantly live at eight-percent body fat with pectorals plumped to the size of twenty-ounce steaks. Women are not meant to have twig-thin arms and bowling ball butts and bosoms.

Since most of the naked bodies we see now come from advertisements—which are notoriously skewed—we get a perverted idea of what a human body is actually like. For a time, I lived with a lingerie designer in Los Angeles—and she would show me how editors photoshopped the (already stunning) models to make them even more appealing. They elongated their legs by several inches, cinched their waists, and doubled the size of their eyes. By the time the editors were done, many of the women were no longer recognizable—yet, a consumer would look at the packaging and not be able to discern how dishonest their depictions actually were. Their mind would remember and compare the advertisements to their own self-images—and they would walk away feeling less-positive about themself.

Without other, real, naked bodies to compare ourselves to in casual social interactions (like public bathing facilities), we are left to study the highly surgicalized, makeuped, steroided, and photoshopped figures in media. In consequence, we feel diminished. We chastise ourselves for not being good enough—when in reality, we might be exactly as we are meant to be. No other creature on the planet shames themself for their God-given appearance—no cheetah longs for spots that are darker or spaced further apart. No elephant wishes that their trunk were longer and slimmer.

We need to recalibrate our connection to social nudity. We need to see that which is normal as being beautiful—and give up worshiping the hyperbolic.

You can witness this shift toward relishing unrealistic extremes by how children's play figurines have changed dimensions over the decades. Much has been written about how Barbie attained impossible proportions in the latter part of the twentieth century—legs, waists, and busts that could not structurally support themselves—inspiring a generation of girls into believing that they were never good enough. Less reported, but similar, has been the unrealistic expectations being sold to boys. When the original Star Wars movies came out, the play figurines closely matched the physiques of the actors on screen. A little over a decade later, by the late nineteen-eighties, the same figurines had suddenly bulked up with dozens of pounds of muscle. The dolls now looked more like Hulk Hogan than Han Solo.

Growing up, I learned that the ideal male body-type was that of the Ninja Turtles and G.I. Joe figurines. I understood that a man's upper arms were supposed to be bigger than his waist; his pecs were supposed to be meatier than his thighs. Combined with the fitness magazine covers showing steroided men, I felt horribly deficient and too thin. I learned to be ashamed of my normal body proportions. I couldn't understand that these Schwarzenegger-like attributes were thoroughly artificial and unattainable.

We so often talk about body dysmorphia in women—and for a good reason. The societal pressure for women to appear perpetually twenty-three, a size two, doe-eyed, and still somehow buxom, is crushing. We have equated the achievement of a thigh-gap with the bliss of nirvana. Americans have come to recognize the persistent and damaging health-effects of advertising on girls and women—and also persons of color. For much of the Westernized world, pale skin and European proportions have been held as an ideal over duskier skin hues and non-Western shapes.

Thankfully, work is being done to combat this bias—but there is still much room to change. Campaigns by Dove USA have opened up awareness and frank conversations—hiring models of color and untraditional beauty or gender identity has been helpful—but there is still a great deal work to be done. We need to embrace beauty in all its forms.

An equally important, but not as well-recognized, issue is the parallel struggle underway for men. Many men feel immense pressure to conform to physiological standards that are likewise unachievable. Self-reported studies conducted with high school students found that up to five percent (of all students, including women) admit to using steroids.[2] If we look at gay men specifically, one in seven admit to using them in just the past year alone.[3]

The ads and movies have convinced men that their worth is in the thickness of their arms. We are told that if you are insufficiently beefy, then you are insufficiently manly. This is one of the puzzle pieces in the rise of toxic masculinity over the past decades (amongst many other stressors, like the loss of the ability to support a household on a single income, well-paid blue- and white-collar jobs, etc.)—men have been repeatedly told that they aren't man-enough for being the way they are. We are supposed to attain impossible standards to be considered sufficient.

Another aspect of popular culture that has led to feelings of male insufficiency is our fascination with oversized penises. The rise in consumption of pornographic material with the advent of the internet has made men more consciously aware of the prodigiously endowed—and the barrage of sexual material has subsequently made us feel increasingly insecure. Even in mainstream media, men repeatedly hear the message that a phallus as thick as a coke-can and as long as a forearm is somehow superior. Whether it be books like *Fifty Shades of Gray* or films like *Girls Trip*, American culture has fetishized male genitals. Similar to what has been done with women's breasts, we've told men that their worth is somehow tied to the difficult-to-change dimensions of their members.

> *"You will never look like the girl in the magazine. The girl in the magazine doesn't even look like the girl in the magazine."*
> — **Jessiemae Peluso, comedian**

Why do we berate ourselves for being perfectly healthy, functional, and beautiful in the way nature intended us? Why do we surround ourselves with a fitness/wellness/beauty culture that makes us sick and mentally unwell? No one is as perfect as social media or advertisements make them appear.

Working as a professional actor, I got to interact with some of the world's top models. Yes, many of them are stunning in person— but even they still have their imperfections. Each human has parts of themself that they wish they could change—asymmetrical or dysfunctional bits that they try to hide. That fitness model you admire, with his bowling-ball-like shoulders, might have acne all over his chest and back that gets edited out in post-production. That beautiful actress leaning on the fireplace mantel at a party might have a hip condition that makes it nearly impossible for her to walk without pain. You, the observer, just don't know about their areas of concern because you don't see them. But I can assure you, everyone has their imperfect parts. There is not one person on this green earth that is flawless—they just seem to be until you get to know them.

But you know what? There is beauty in that imperfection. There is gorgeousness in unfiltered humanity. You are raw; you are perfect; you are exactly the sort of person the world needs, just as you are.

> *"If we make self-love or body acceptance conditional, the truth is, we will never be happy with ourselves. The reality is that our bodies are constantly changing, and they will never remain exactly the same. If we base our self-worth on something as ever-changing as our bodies, we will forever be on the emotional roller coaster of body obsession and shame."*
> — **Chrissy King, fitness coach**

EXERCISE

It's time to see what other people's bodies really look like—offline. If you are anything like me, you grew up in a world where social nudity was taboo. To counter this, we need to find places where we can learn to be amongst others in our unadorned states. One of my favorite venues for such is a Korean spa—institutions that have become quite common across America. In addition to having numerous saunas made out of mud, rock salt, gemstones, or charcoal—they also have gender-segregated pool areas where bathers are required to be naked. I recommend finding out if there are any such facilities nearby.

If you are traveling to Europe, look for saunas (be sure to verify before going that they aren't the "sexy" kind...unless that's what you're intentionally looking for—in which case, more power to you) that have steam rooms and thermal baths. Another Stateside option, but a bit harder to find nowadays, is a gym with open locker room showers—or even just a culture that isn't towel and stall-obsessed. YMCAs and university gyms are usually better when pertaining to social nudity than big-box gyms. While you're visiting, spend some time examining what other bodies really look like.

If you're feeling tremendously brave, consider hosting a "body beautiful" party where you invite your friends over to sip rosé in the buff. The first time my childhood friends and I hung out together naked—at a Korean spa, incidentally—we felt a deeper level of closeness and kinship with each other, even though we'd already been friends for more than a dozen years.

It is almost impossible to feel one-hundred-percent transparent with another person if you are always protected by clothes. Nudity is a great leveler—it decreases external symbols of status and increases a shared sense of humanity. We bare our flaws and prove that everyone has them. Once you've explored social nudity, please journal about your experience below. I hope you find it revelatory and healing.

My experience with social nudity:

_____
_____
_____
_____
_____
_____
_____
_____
_____
_____
_____
_____
_____
_____
_____
_____
_____
_____

> *"There's something therapeutic about nudity.*
> *Take away the Gucci or Levi's, and we're all the same."*
> — **Kevin Bacon, American actor**

There is an unfortunate fantasy that we can get caught up in: if only I became incredibly beautiful, my life would be so much better. We are sold this idea that a stylish wardrobe, a perfectly symmetrical face, and a streamlined body will grant us lasting peace and happiness. In reality, this couldn't be further from the truth. Having worked in the entertainment industry, I can confirm that there is an inordinately high level of depression, anxiety, anorexia, drug use, and self-abuse in the extraordinarily beautiful community.

Too often, people see individuals on the far-end of the attractiveness spectrum as being commodities—objects to make money off of or use. The acquaintances I've known who exist as an "eleven out of ten" often ache from being treated as an object and not as a feeling-and-thinking person. I remember one model I worked with confiding in me that she liked to cut herself with knives because it "ruined the real estate." When you're regularly viewed as something otherworldly, you are no longer regarded as a relatable human being. This level of beauty is often more of a curse than a blessing—and something I would be wary of wishing on anyone.

We should be conscious of choosing our friends, colleagues, and partners for their character rather than for their luscious hair or pouty lips. We need people in our lives that light up our intelligence and tingle our imaginations. We have to learn to give value based on hearts, minds, and spirits—not just on external parts. Similarly, we need to value ourselves based on our internal state of being and put less emphasis on our bodily statures.

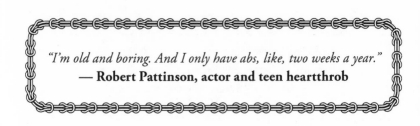

The more dissatisfied someone feels about themself—the more disconnected they are from their sense of inner-worth—the more they'll often use external means to achieve validation. Too many people relentlessly tweak their bodies to make them feel better about their sense of selfhood. Whether through facial fillers, implants, liposuction, or fad diets—we believe that a prettier exterior will make us feel more complete as a whole. This is simply false.

Bigger muscles or smaller waistlines will not inspire people to genuinely love you more or make you more satisfied with your life. Achieving extreme beauty or fitness goals often accompanies greater insecurity, in fact. People who attain the heights of physical fitness often discover a sudden drive to go even further—along with an obsessive need to maintain whatever has already been gained. Soon, people start skipping time with family and friends to go to the gym. They avoid meals out with loved ones because they can't bear eating off-diet. They opt out of exotic trips abroad because they are afraid of disrupting their intense wellness regimens. I know a fitness model who will refuse to leave his house for a week if he goes one night off-diet; he is too ashamed of how he looks and what people will think of him.

Gaining an amazing physique only makes a person feel like they need to go even further, become even more cut. Part of the addictive quality of steroids is the fact that users can't imagine going back to having a natural physique—their whole identity has become entwined with looking a certain way. Even knowing that they are injecting chemicals that will ultimately shorten their lifespan significantly, few are able to give them up. Fulfilling aesthetic goals often exacerbates the feeling of not being good enough—because there is always someone fitter, more beautiful, or younger with whom to compare. We have to soothe our inner fears and replace our sense of lack with affirmations of our worth and value.

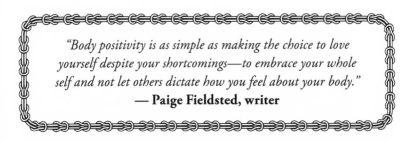

> "Body positivity is as simple as making the choice to love yourself despite your shortcomings—to embrace your whole self and not let others dictate how you feel about your body."
> — **Paige Fieldsted, writer**

On the topic of men, muscles, and masculinity—there are some out there who pose the notion that perhaps the need to appear hyper-masculine comes from a deep insecurity regarding sexuality and gender identity. A former steroid-user and aspiring filmmaker, Brock Yurich, explores the relentless dissatisfaction of many bodybuilders—and suggests that many muscle-giants are actually closeted gay men who use their bodies to compensate for feelings of lacking requisite maleness. Young men learn early on that if they do not feel masculine enough, bigger muscles can provide a brick wall to hide behind and to keep other men from doubting or questioning them.

Imagine being a young boy who realizes that he is not like his older brothers—he feels deficient because he is not as rough-and-tumble or skirt-chasing as the "manly men" in his family. He recognizes that he might be queer—and what's the easiest solution to avoid detection and shaming? Adopt hyper-masculinity in his appearance and demeanor—become a swaggering jock with as "swole" muscles as possible.

The trans-identified bodybuilder, Janae Marie Kroczaleski, has a self-examining Netflix documentary, *Transformer*, on just this topic. For most of her life, she craved getting bigger as a way to compensate for feeling fraudulent as a man. In her forties, the contradiction between her body and her identity reached a crisis point. She could no longer uphold the persona she'd been projecting and finally transitioned to presenting as female. She still body-builds and flaunts her size as a thought-provoking contradiction for what society says women should look like. It's been a long and painful struggle for her to come to terms with the fact that much of her life was spent hiding who she really is.

> *"We are not what other people say we are. We are who we know ourselves to be, and we are what we love. That's OK."*
> — **Laverne Cox, actress and trans activist**

Many young men use the performance of hyper-masculinity as a way to survive in a world that does not hold space for men to express affection, tenderness, or empathy. Many communities in America demand that men present as being extraordinarily masculine and women demonstrably feminine. In doing so, people are forced to deny any parts of themselves that do not fit within these narrow and constraining stereotypes. Forcing men to subjugate aspects of themselves can inspire anger, confusion, and emotional repression. It then becomes a short trip from demonstrating hyper-masculinity to the dangerous land of enacting toxic masculinity.

Toxic masculinity is the performance of maleness to such a degree that one viciously attacks anyone or anything that challenges or doubts a man's credentials. It is infused with rage—a fear of being found out or for lacking requisite power—and it often shows its nastiest sides when the man interacts with those who can be easily dominated. If a woman isn't deferring enough—shut her down. If a man shows any form of vulnerability—break him down. Perform macho-ness, perform entitlement—hide anything that reveals weakness or perceived femininity.

The reality is that all humans possess both masculine and feminine aspects. In fact, some of the most well-adjusted, masculine-presenting men I've known have been immensely kind, compassionate, and tender. Instead of teaching boys that masculinity means titanium-like strength, we need to teach them that it also means flexibility and a willingness to listen and learn. Instead of teaching that being a man means rugged individualism, we need to prove that it can also mean connection to community, artistic expression, and empathy. Enacting maleness can require breaking, smashing, and destroying—but it can also demand times of building, cultivating, and caregiving. Our goal needs to be the attainment of wholeness—a coming into acceptance with all of our attributes, not just one side.

Going back to my argument from an earlier chapter, that gender exists in spectrums—I will suggest that there is no right way to express masculinity or femininity. Feminine women can still be ambitious, hard-hitting, and powerful. Masculine men can still be empathetic, vulnerable, and reflective. All genders can express all of these feelings.

Women, of course, also have immense pressure to conform to societal standards—I have coached women in leadership roles at major corporations for several years and can affirm that they have to walk an impossible tightrope that is invisible to men. As we can see with female politicians, when women try to enact traditionally masculine-associated attributes like claiming authority or giving orders, there can be tremendous pushback. Society doesn't hold space for women to be angry, powerful, or authoritative in the way that they do men. They do not permit them to be ambitious, financially successful, or commanding in the way they laud men for being.

Regarding sexual expression, however, women are sometimes given more leeway to express their sexual orientation. From Katy Perry's song, "I Kissed a Girl," to the prevalence of woman-on-woman porn made specifically for male consumption, there is less eyebrow-raising in American society when women explore sexual interactions with varied genders. Men, by contrast, appear to be more confined in the ways they are permitted to explore. Once a man participates in male-centric sexual exploration, he will often be excommunicated from the cult macho-ness—he will henceforth be labeled "queer" or a "faggot." A woman can supposedly be permitted to have numerous adventures with other women and comfortably be invited back into the fold of heteronormative womanhood—their actions labeled mere experimentation. But a man can never go back. He will forevermore be known as "gay"—which is why there are so many "straight men" who have sex with men. Go to any bathhouse at four o'clock in the afternoon, and you'll see that the predominate clientele is self-described heterosexuals who are looking to get off with another dude.

Throughout the twentieth century, lesbian partners drew far less ire than gay men. In the words of comedian Hannah Gadsby, "In all the debate about homosexuality, no one ever really talked about the lesbians. [...T]hey're like, 'What even are they? What do they do, though, really? Do they even exist if no one's watching? No, don't worry about them. No harm in a cuddle.' For a long time, I knew more facts about unicorns than I did about lesbians." Society is less concerned with what women do with their nether bits than what men do.

In the Western world, men have to defend their maleness in a way than women do not—they have to show that they are "man enough," tough, and rugged—and disavow any actions that might discredit those labels. I will argue that anyone living in a state of self-protection will not be at home in themselves. Any man or woman who has to be "on guard" will subsequently be ill-at-ease. They will likely make an insufficient lover, spouse, or parent because they will be afraid to express themselves in their entirety.

For their partners, trying to build a life with another person who is only using a small slice of their identity will be frustrating. It'll be like trying to walk beside someone who insists on only using one of their legs, though they have two. By contrast, a person who can embrace all of themself—queerness and all (because we are *all* queer in some way)—will be able to live with heightened integrity, respect, and grace. By embracing all of our parts—we find inner peace, belonging, and deeper joy.

EXERCISE

We are again going to turn to someone outside of ourselves to assist in our growth. For this exercise, call someone who you trust and know well—and ask if they'd be willing to have a candid conversation with you about body-image. Share that you are coming to realize that you have some unhealthy perceptions about your body—and you'd like to hear about their own experiences managing physical dissatisfaction/shame.

Nearly every person struggles with their accepting their exterior—and the more you're willing to express your feelings, the better you will ultimately feel. Remember the quotation I shared earlier by sociologist Brené Brown: "Shame derives its power by being unspeakable." Once you name your fears and realize that you're not the only one, it will become easier to heal. Be gutsy and risk being vulnerable.

Again, this conversation should happen with someone who will appreciate your candor, be able to reciprocate, and be capable of holding confidentiality. Always remember that you can seek the help of a health professional if your struggles are weighty. Eating disorders and self-harming behaviors are outside the scope of peer mentorship and require medical guidance.

188

Here are some suggestions on how to begin the conversation:

- *I realize that I haven't been as kind to my body as I would like. Do you have any tips or tricks that you use to be kinder with yourself?*
- *I am coming to terms with the fact that I feel shame around parts of my body. I want to learn to accept myself as I am. How have you dealt with body-image issues in the past? I'd like some support.*
- *Do you ever feel like there are times where you feel ugly? I sometimes feel like I'm the only one who thinks that about themself.*
- *What are some ways you promote a positive body image for yourself? I am discovering that I could be doing a lot better with my self-talk.*

When you are done, journal about your experiences below.

Discussing Body Shame:

_____

_____

_____

_____

_____

_____

_____

_____

_____

_____

_____

_____

_____

_____

_____

_____

_____

_____

_____

_____

_____

_____
_____
_____
_____
_____
_____
_____
_____
_____
_____
_____

> "As a child, I never heard one woman say to me, 'I love my body.'
> Not my mother, my elder sister, my best friend. No one woman
> has ever said, 'I am so proud of my body.' So I make sure to say
> it to my daughter because a positive physical outlook has to start
> at an early age."
> — **Kate Winslet, actress**

We all have areas that we nitpick—parts of ourselves that we fantasize about hiring a surgeon or a dermatologist to correct. Instead of continuing this narrative of "I am not enough" or "I am imperfect as I am," we need to celebrate ourselves as we are. It's impossible to truthfully say that "I fully love and accept myself" when in the next breath we add, "but my thighs are disgusting." We need to cherish all of our parts—even the saggy, puffy, wobbly, cottage-cheesy bits.

We need to embrace ourselves as we currently are without reservations. Perhaps, one day, you will get super fit. Maybe you will join the gym, lose fifty pounds, get a modeling contract for a protein-supplement company. But whether or not that day comes, you have to learn to accept yourself as you are. If you are always living for a day in the future when you will have attained *xyz*, I promise that, when/if the day comes, having achieved that goal will still not feel good-enough. The experience won't be as affirming as you hoped.

We have to let go of the notion that some external goal will fulfill us. You could be one of the most beautiful and fittest people on your block, but you could still feel ugly enough to be afraid of leaving your house. No amount of external striving will provide you with a lasting sensation of sufficiency. If you are reliant on an arbitrary tape measurement or scale reading to give you permission to accept yourself—you will forever be in terror of relapsing.

Cultivating body-positivity can begin with changing our responses to how we take in our reflections and pictures of ourselves. Too often, we use negative self-talk to describe what we see—"Look how scrawny my arms look" or "Ugh, who would ever want a girl with legs the size of tree trunks." Stop the self-abuse! Each nasty word or unkind expression buries into our subconscious—it creates further fear and disconnection from ourselves.

Ask yourself, when has shaming someone ever created lasting, positive change? A dog that is slapped or berated for peeing inside the house may stop for a week—but will then find hidden or secret places to urinate. It acts out. By comparison, if you quietly redirect a pup to piddle outside—and praise them for doing so—they will potty-train much more easily and effectively. And they won't end up being neurotic and biting you on the leg. Inspiring shame only makes creatures more unhappy, more unwell. Shame builds resentment and hate for whatever inspires the negative feelings. Instead, let's think and act kindly toward ourselves—let's make changes from a place of positivity and affirmation.

In the moments when you catch yourself making unkind remarks about your appearance or behaviors, find something to compliment yourself on instead. When you walk past a mirror, purposefully encourage yourself to smile. When a friend posts a photo of you on Facebook, notice one aspect that you can genuinely appreciate about yourself before clicking onward.

191

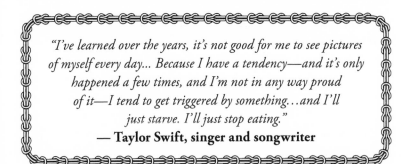

Growing up, I felt tremendous shame around the shape of my chest. I was born with a deformity called *pectus excavatum*—meaning that my sternum and front ribs curve inward rather than out. As a boy, I was a member of the local swim team—and other children would point and tease me, asking why I had a "hole in my chest." I experienced profound shame around my appearance—I quickly learned to avoid baring my atypical sternum in public. As soon as a race would finish, I would hurriedly climb out of the pool and rush to don a shirt or wrap myself in a towel. For years, I would hurry to change in locker rooms so people wouldn't notice my physiological difference.

This is probably part of the reason that I craved bigger muscles—I figured that if I became brawny-enough, my thoracic deformation would be less apparent. I hoped the big pecs would hide my concave chest. Ironically, the universe seemed to have other ideas.

My shoulders are hypermobile, which means that I face instability and frequent injuries to these joints. This made it challenging for me to regularly work out my pecs as a young man—pushups and bench presses caused considerable pain and prolonged recovery time. My karma forced me to face my emotional discomfort rather than be able to hide it.

Over time, I have become much more comfortable with myself as I am. My ribcage shape no longer causes me anxiety like it used to, but I am still aware of its uniqueness. Instead of dwelling on feelings of inadequacy, however, I thank my body for being healthy, strong, and—in its own unique way—beautiful. My husband shows me that he finds me attractive—and his appreciation of me has helped me heal even further. Now, when someone asks me about my chest, I don't get the same jolt of terror that I used to. Instead, I just simply mention that it is congenital and move along.

I'll freely admit, I have not yet fully arrived at the goal of complete self-love and wild contentment with my appearance—but I am much better than I used to be. I no longer pick at every little pimple in the way I did in years prior—I am now also more freely comfortable with my unclothed body. I am a work in progress and am doing my best to appreciate myself as best as I am able. Each of us has to cultivate genuine gratitude for the bodies we have been given—for they are the only ones we are going to get in this lifetime.

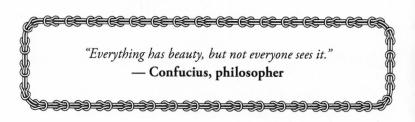

"Everything has beauty, but not everyone sees it."
— **Confucius, philosopher**

MEDITATION IX

Close your eyes and examine your breath. Find a deep sense of centeredness, allowing yourself to be wherever you are—allowing yourself to find a sense of home in whatever space you find yourself.

When you are ready, gently turn your focus to a part of yourself that you've labeled as being less than desirable. Hone in on a section of your anatomy that you've decided is un-lovable.

As you focus in this area, quietly say to it: "I love you. You are perfect as you are. Thank you for being a part of me."

This might bring up feelings of discomfort—we are so used to chastising our cellulite, berating our love-handles, shaming our lumpy bits. Instead—speak kindness to these parts. Tell them that you love them. Even if that feels scary—tell all your shameful bits that you are glad that they are there.

So long as you keep categorizing parts of yourself as being "wrong" or "ugly" or even just "unattractive," you will perpetually be at war with yourself. So tell your fat that you love it. Tell your too-small or too-big or too-wrinkly sections that you are glad that they are there. Even if fear comes up for you—keep going. You have to find peace with all of yourself.

Telling these "less-attractive" parts that they're beautiful won't make them grow bigger. Telling your acne that you embrace its presence won't make it hang around longer. Instead, it'll give you the freedom to truly be where you are—to make peace with your present condition.

Next, imagine a full-length mirror propped up in front of you— and imagine yourself standing naked in front of it. Don't change your body. Don't erase bits or morph them—let everything be exactly as it is right now. Smile at your reflection. Tell yourself how beautiful you are. Keep reassuring yourself that you are perfect, lovable, and healthy. Thank your body for all the amazing things it does. Stay with this image until you can really accept these messages of self-acceptance at a deep level.

Learning to love your body doesn't mean that you can't also make strides to alter it. If you struggle with your weight—yes, you may need to change, but you need to do so from a place of love. You cannot shame yourself into being fit. You can't berate yourself into good health. Lead from compassion—lead from love. Accept where you are, and gently make progress from there.

You are whole. You are perfect. Love yourself for where you're at right now. Let this moment be enough. Let you, as you are, be thoroughly enough.

> "Physical fitness is not only one of the most important keys to a healthy body, it is the basis of dynamic and creative intellectual activity."
> — **John F. Kennedy, American President**

Appreciating our bodies with positive thoughts is important—but we also need to take care of them. Positive thoughts on their own will not allow us to fully love the skin we are in—we also have to be tender stewards of these amazing physical forms. As much as I claim that wellness comes from within, we also need to acknowledge that health and fitness are critical ingredients to mental and emotional wellbeing.

While I have a tendency to say that appearances don't matter—like with everything, the opposite is also true. We want to be able to smile when we look in the mirror—we ought to do the best we can with what we have been given. A healthy body can be the precursor to a healthy disposition. We do not want to overly fixate on appearances, but—at the same time—we should strive to develop ourselves as best as we can.

I know for myself, getting a good pump at the gym, finding stability in a new yoga pose, or discovering that my t-shirt arms feel a touch snugger—all make me feel proud of my body. Being able to run a distance that never seemed achievable, conquering a precarious mountain hike, or getting back into that outfit you wore at a special moment in your life—these are all things that can create a genuine sense of well-being. It feels good to know that we have the agency to achieve our goals, to take care of ourselves, and to make beneficial change.

The trick is to do these things and simultaneously let go of the results. Forgive ourselves for failing to attain anything that is outside of our natural propensity or genetic disposition. If you are naturally curvy, then you may always be curvy—you shouldn't berate yourself about it. Do the best you can to keep your bodyweight in line and then be kind to yourself about the results. Let go of a specific outcome. Do your part, but allow yourself to be as you are.

By taking care of our bodies, we show respect and love for ourselves, body and soul. When you exercise, when you move, you are thanking your body for all the amazing things that it does. You are nourishing it, stretching it. Each time you run on an open track or a treadmill can be an act of wild devotion for these amazing physical forms. Each yoga pose or dance move can be an expression of ecstatic appreciation. By taking care of ourselves, we demonstrate love for ourselves. And as we feel better about how we look, move, and exist within our bodies—it becomes easier to love ourselves even more.

I realize that much of this may sound contradictory to my proclamations earlier in the chapter about not getting overly focused on our external appearances. While that is very much true, the reality is that we do not exist independently of our flesh. If you continuously feel bad about yourself, it's going to be challenging to love the skin you're in. So, yes—love yourself emphatically. Embrace your wonky bits, your stretched-out parts, and your saggy sections. But also, do what you can to make your body the radiant, sacred vessel that it is. After all, as many have said, we are spirits having a bodily experience. We need to adore and show respect to these temples we call home.

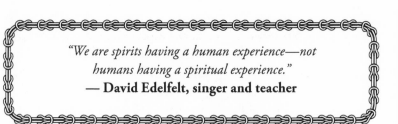

One of the best things we can do for our health is to move each and every day. Physical motion provides a host of benefits for our bodies and minds, including reducing stress, breaking down blockages, and getting the blood pumping. A simple, but effective, way to do this is simply by going on walks. Studies have shown that even thirty minutes of walking a day can have a significant impact on the immune, cardiovascular, lymphatic, and nervous systems—it even reduces the risk of major depression by twenty-six percent.[4] It's something that can be done any time: first thing in the morning, during a lunch break, or before bed.

By getting our bodies moving, we break apart natural adhesions that form each night when we go to sleep. If you feel up for a queasy experience, check out the videos of Gill Hedley. He is a researcher who graphically demonstrates the effects of immobility. He shows real human cadavers—bodies that moved daily and ones that kept parts of themselves physically bound due to injury or habitual holding patterns.

In the bodies that moved daily, he demonstrates that little adhesions that look like fuzz naturally form and then dissolve with stretching and active motion. With the bodies that did not move sufficiently, that fuzz builds upon itself—eventually becoming inelastic sheaths of tissue that bind structures down. The soft, gliding surfaces like tendon, fascia, and muscle are unable to move effectively—leading to pain, limited range of motion, and disease for the person.[5]

We have to take care of ourselves. We ought to spend time daily to move, stretch, and sweat. I am personally a fan of physical practices that help to encourage a mind-body connection like yoga, tai chi, qigong, kung fu, or the like—but really, any form of exercise can be beneficial. The range of what I personally explore varies from restorative yoga to high-intensity plyometric exercises. Some days I bend my body into a pretzel—other days I walk vigorously with my dog—others, I pick up heavy things and gently set them back down.

Regardless, I try to approach each time I move my body as a celebration of being alive. I thank my body for all that it does. And I tell it that it's beautiful—even if it's not exactly what I wished it would be. I remind myself of the artificiality of many of the figures I see in media—and encourage myself to see wholeness just as I am. I strive to be as healthy and fit as my body is capable of being—and forgive myself of any perceived shortcomings. That's my goal, anyways. I do my best—and forget the rest.

I encourage you to adopt a similar vantage. Find a way of moving that makes you feel good—and worry less about the results. Exercise for health, longevity, and vibrancy—and love yourself no matter what. You are perfect—you are beautiful. No matter what size you wear.

> *"Exercise releases endorphins—endorphins make you happy.*
> *Happy people don't kill their husbands—they just don't."*
> **— Elle Woods in the film *Legally Blonde***

EXERCISE

Time to exercise and move. Take a Pilates class, go for a run, hike a trail, swim laps, dance like no one's watching, pick up something heavy and push it around. Do something approachable, affordable, and fun.

It's important to find a fitness regimen that is easy to access so you can return to it again and again. Aim for thirty minutes of movement each day, if at all possible. You can refine your workout plan over time—but take on a form of exercise that you can start right away and commit to. Strive to keep it up for sixty-eight days straight so you can establish the neural pathways necessary to turn this practice into a habit.

Eastern healing modalities generally recommend that we exercise until we reach the point that we sweat along our spine, under our arms, and on our chests—and then stop. Despite the recent fitness crazes encouraging us to exercise as if it were a zombie apocalypse—like our lives are depending on it—it may not actually be healthy. Ayurvedic and traditional Chinese Medicine say that it is a detriment to our overall health to workout so hard. Don't exercise to the point of exhaustion—just make sure you move and get glistening. In the words of a former trainer, "Keep it light—keep it happy—keep it fun."

When I think about exercise, I feel _____
_____
_____
_____
_____
_____
_____
_____

I would like to get to the point that exercise makes me feel___
_____
_____
_____
_____
_____

I would like my body to be able to functionally do_____
_____

_____

_____

Based on my goals, these modes of exercise might be beneficial:

_____

_____

_____

_____

Suggestions include: *running, walking, dancing, jump-roping, playing a sport, surfing, weight lifting, aerobics, bike riding, yoga, tai chi, qigong, power lifting, gymnastics, martial arts, boxing, climbing stairs, group fitness class, active stretching, swimming, acrobatics, plyometrics, rowing, Pilates, hiking, kettlebells, rock climbing, kayaking, sports.*

I am going to aim to exercise daily, ideally at the same time. The best time for me is _____ in the morning/evening (circle one). I will complete sixty-eight days of movement on this date: _____.

One of the easiest, cheapest, and most beneficial forms of exercise—which you can practice anywhere, and that requires no equipment—is yoga. In addition to getting you moving, flexible, and aerobically engaged, yoga also stimulates the parasympathetic nervous system—a sort of neurological "brake pedal" that shuts down the stress response and allows your body to heal. Doing even just the six most essential yoga poses can have a positive effect. I highly encourage you to make them a part of your practice.

"Yoga is the journey of the self to the self, through the self."
— **The Bhagavad Gita**

Try to match the shapes of each pose without too much effort—we want to release tension rather than build it. Endeavor to hold each pose for five to ten breaths, if possible. You can go through this sequence of six poses either once or multiple times. Keep your mind focused on your body and breath as much as is possible.

Downward Dog (left figure above)

Place your hands on the floor and extend out into a plank pose. From there, keeping a tiny micro-bend in your knees, reach your heels toward the floor and your hips toward the sky. Pull your shoulders wide and down, away from your hands—keep your hands pressed flatly into the floor.

Upward Dog (right figure above)

From downward dog, let your hips drop toward the floor and lift your chest skywards. Pull your shoulder blades toward each other and allow the chest to broaden. Press your hands firmly into the earth, drawing your collarbones away from your ears. Keep the pads of your toes on the floor—or point your toes fully, letting the tops of your feet rest on the floor.

Warrior I (left figure above)

From standing, spread your feet wide apart. Turn your torso (starting at the hips and keeping your spine and shoulders straight) toward one leg, which will now be your front leg, and rotate that foot to point directly forward—allow the back foot to stay turned in. Bend your front knee so that it comes into alignment directly over your ankle—the back leg should stay straight. Square the hips toward the front and extend your arms overhead, keeping your shoulders low and broad.

Warrior II (right figure above)

From warrior I, open your hips ninety-degrees to the side and drop your arms to a T-position. Gaze at your front fingertips.

Standing Forward Fold (left figure above)

Stand with the insides of your feet touching together and a micro-bend in your knees. Exhale and reach down toward the floor, keeping the back of your neck elongated.

Skywards Reach (right figure above)

Stand with your feet together and extend your arms overhead, letting the palms touch one another. Raise up onto your toes and attempt to keep your balance.

Repeat this sequence—feeling free to add any other desired poses—as many times as you'd enjoy. Rest and observe your experience once you feel like it is complete.

As you find a sense of home inside your body, you'll come to appreciate it increasingly more. You'll marvel at the amazing things your body can do and how it has an intelligence of its own. It can let you know when you are sensing danger, when you are titillated, when you are in love. A twinge in your gut, a burst of sweat, a heart palpitation—these are all subtle cues that the body gives us. Listen to them. Let your physical form become a beloved friend.

When you are able to love your body unequivocally, you will know belonging. You will know wellness. You will know home. Strive to strengthen and open your bodily mechanism as best as you are able—simultaneously forgiving it and accepting it for whatever it is. You are whole. You are beautiful. You are unique beyond measure. Love yourself for where you are. Accept yourself as being, as Rumi says, "starlight wrapped in skin."

> *"Everyone should consider his body as a priceless gift from one whom he loves above all, a marvelous work of art, of indescribable beauty, and mystery beyond human conception."*
> — **Nikola Tesla, Inventor**

SUMMARY:

— **Each body has faults, so never envy another person's. Find perfection in the imperfections.**

— **Accept yourself for where you are. When you find a sense of belonging in your body, you'll find belonging within yourself.**

— **Move daily—and explore ways to settle into yourself through conscious movement.**

Chapter 8:

SWAPPING CAMPFIRE TALES

> *"Handle them carefully, for words have
> more power than atom bombs."*
> — **Pearl Strachan Hurd, American politician and writer**

W e all make up stories to tell ourselves—for good or for ill. And the words we choose to tell them are powerful. Stories influence our wellbeing and our connection to our inner selves. If you are unkind with your words, you will feel the results. Our bodies internalize their vibrations. If you repeatedly call yourself "stupid," "inept," or "lazy"—you will likely feel discomfort within. Inversely, if you call yourself "kind," "loving," and "forgiving," inner peace will have a chance to take root.

At the turn of the twentieth century, a photographer and hobbyist scientist named Masaru Emoto self-published a book entitled *Messages From Water*. In it, he shared photographs of dozens of water crystals that he froze in his lab. According to Emoto, he would write a word on the container—and once the water droplets were frozen, the dishes inscribed with negative-sounding words were found to have crystals that were asymmetrical, dull, or lacking complicated shapes. The containers marked with uplifting words mainly contained rainbow-hued, ornate, and symmetrical snowflakes inside.

His argument was that the vibrations inherent to the words on the Petri dishes could change the shapes the water droplets took—and since the human body is sixty percent water, paying attention to the words we use can similarly transform us. While his methods were not meticulously recorded or peer-reviewed, nor has anyone replicated his findings in a laboratory setting with concrete results—there has been anecdotal evidence that his research has merit. Certainly, countless individuals on social media have taken his ideas and explored them with enthusiasm—posting their findings with gusto and emphatic declarations of success.

Regardless of whether or not he was exaggerating his claims—I do believe that there is value in his argument. Anyone who grew up in an environment where they were regularly called "good-for-nothing," "a mistake," or "disappointing" will tell you how deeply internalized those feelings became. And—unequivocally—we know that the quality of the thoughts resounding inside our brain will have a commensurate effect on our physiology. If we think negatively, our bodies will feel ill at ease.

A study by Richard Davidson at the University of Wisconsin—Madison, showed that people thinking discouraging thoughts while being injected with a vaccine produced far fewer antibodies than a control group.[1] In just this one example, pessimistic words in peoples' heads measurably depleted their immune systems. Other studies have linked repeated negative self-talk with depression, increased rates of illness, and slower response times to stimuli.[2]

We have to be careful with the words we choose because those words will change us. Now, I'm not someone who believes that a person will mutate into whatever they repeat—I am not going to suggest that by making a mantra out of "I'm a six-foot, seven-inch basketball star," I will suddenly turn into LeBron James. But I am going to argue that words carry vibrations, and those vibrations have the power to shape reality. If you look at many of the world's esoteric faith traditions, practitioners and scholars hold a deep regard for the energy invested in the words.

From Brahmins studying *mantrika shakti* in the Indian spiritual traditions to Kabbalah scholars devoting entire careers to investigating why the Torah begins with the second letter of the Hebrew alphabet and not the first—people across time have observed the ability of words to alter the perceivable world. If everything breaks down into energy—quarks, atoms, and light waves—what is sound but another force of change?

A direct way to witness this power is to observe how people change over time based on the words they use. Meditation teacher and scholar, Dr. Lorin Roche, shares a story about a woman he coached who had been repeating the word "down" as a self-chosen mantra, thinking it would help her calm and relax. Over time, she reported feeling increasingly more depressed. That state became all-consuming until Dr. Roche invited her to change the word she kept repeating—and when she did, her mental state elevated in response.[3]

For myself, there were periods of my life that I would use word repetition to alter my state of being—to frustrating results. I would whisper words to myself like "successful," "talented," "worthy"—but they wouldn't take hold. Over time, I came to understand that, deeper down, there were subconscious mantras that proclaimed the opposite. Words like "inadequate," "unlovable," "failure," and "disappointment" reverberated within the pit of my psyche. Even though my conscious mind strove to uplift, the quicksand in my subconscious sucked everything downward. It took many years of meditation and self-excavation to root out that harmful vocabulary and sow words of acceptance and kindness in their place.

What are the words that are lingering within your deeper mind? And how do they relate to the person you want to be? Again, I am not encouraging you to engage in whimsical wish-fulfillment ("I'm a unicorn! I'm a unicorn!"). I am asking you to articulate how you want to be, how you want to feel—and let the vibration inherent in those words guide you into that. I suggest that you start using words like "easeful," "relaxed," "authentic," "at peace." Use language that describes the qualities you want to cultivate and that also feel intrinsically aligned with your essence. Don't try to will yourself into being someone you're not. Choose vocabulary that connects you with your most authentic self.

> *"If a person has ugly thoughts, it begins to show on the face. And when that person has ugly thoughts every day, every week, every year, the face gets uglier and uglier until you can hardly bear to look at it. [...] But if you have good thoughts, they will s hine out of your face like sunbeams, and you will always look lovely."*
> — **Roald Dahl, children's writer and poet**

EXERCISE

What are the qualities that you feel are integral to your identity? What attributes would you like to shine at the forefront? Who are you, really? Create a list of whatever you believe accurately reflects your truth.

I am...

_____   _____   _____

_____   _____   _____

_____   _____   _____

_____ _____ _____
_____ _____ _____
_____ _____ _____
_____ _____ _____
_____ _____ _____
_____ _____ _____
_____ _____ _____
_____ _____ _____
_____ _____ _____

Let's narrow this list down to the top three. Please put stars next to your contenders and rewrite your top three descriptors below.

_____ _____ _____

_____ _____ _____

Are you aware of any negative self-talk that should be mitigated? If there is, please don't chastise yourself and thereby reinforce those negative patterns. Instead, calmly redirect your language—be affirming rather than discouraging.

I am not going to ask you to write those unhappy words out—because, again, words have power, and scribing them increases their influence. Instead, I am going to ask you to analyze the moments when unkind self-talk rears its head. What are the specific moments when you find yourself needing to change your language? Moments of rushing, unexpected stress, or heightened distractions can be when negative self-talk occurs.

I am most unkind to myself when...

_____

_____

_____

"Speak only if it improves upon the silence."
— **Mahatma Gandhi, social activist and spiritual leader**

Covering the gamut of prayers, mantras, sacred chants, and devotional songs, faith traditions throughout time have recognized the power of repeated words or phrases to uplift and inspire. Perhaps you grew up in a household that encouraged you to offer prayers before dinner or turning in to bed—maybe you were born to meditative parents that had you recite a mantra to the click of meditation beads. Or, perhaps, you had a family song that everyone sang that bonded you all together. These consciously chosen phrases can be a way of harmonizing and drawing uplifting vibrations into our lives.

Earlier in the book, I encouraged you to repeat the phrase "I am enough" as you went about your day. Did you try it? How did it feel? Was there any sort of internal shift that occurred for you?

I would like to build upon this idea of a chosen phrase—and I invite you to make one for yourself that can be repeated over and again. A set of words that will help you cultivate the vibration you desire. Some examples of a personal mantra could include:

I am beautiful, I am radiant, I belong.

I am grateful for all the blessings in my life.

I am grounded and rooted into my truth.

I am whole, I am perfect, I am loving.

I am authentically me—I am proud of who I am.

I am strong, I am bold, I can handle anything that comes.

I am relaxed, I am at peace, I am flowing.

I am enough.

These are launching-off points for you to find your own personal-empowerment phrase. It can be anything you want—as long as it involves words that you believe are integral to you. Don't attempt to turn yourself into something you're not—learn to love and accept yourself for who you are at your essence. Develop the best version of you.

> *"Stop acting so small. You are the universe in ecstatic motion."*
> — **Rumi, Sufi poet and philosopher**

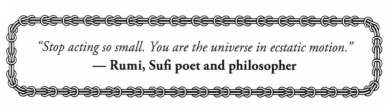

EXERCISE

Dream up your personal mantra. What are the core words that harmonize you with your innate vibration? Please explore a few variations in order to come up with one that feels most deeply aligned.

_____

_____

_____

_____

_____

_____

_____

_____

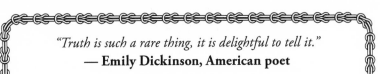

As we focus on our word choices, it is critical that we become aware of our capacity to be truthful. Anytime we communicate something that feels authentic and intrinsically aligned, it will bring us closer to our essence. Whenever we speak words that feel inauthentic or inherently false, it will drive a wedge between us and our innate selfhood. In order to access our ecstatic nature, we need to be radically honest—both internally and with others.

When we say something that we believe, we develop trust with ourselves. If we say, "I will feed my belly at six o'clock"—and we do—our body learns to relax into knowing that we will follow-through. We learn that we are our own best friend—someone that we can rely on, even in difficult times. By contrast, if we forge agreements and subsequently break them—we teach our bodies to be wary of our words. It happens all the time. We tell ourselves that we will stop after just two cookies—but we don't. We tell our bodies that this will be the last time we do that thing that causes us emotional strife and hardship—but we find ourselves doing it again next weekend. Trust is built or deconstructed in the tiny vows we make or break throughout the day.

If you tell yourself something, commit to it and then follow through. Say what you mean to say—do what you pledge to do. Avoid speaking half-truths, white lies, or easily misinterpreted facts—they are all forms of lying. Your subconscious mind will be aware of your intended deceit and will, in turn, trust you less. If your body knows that you befuddle the truth through complex arguments or saying one thing but really meaning another, you will eventually feel internal disconnection.

This form of self-truthfulness is known as integrity. It is living up to the standards you set for yourself—fully inhabiting the person you claim to be. It is backing up your words with actions that are congruent with your intent. "Integrity is telling myself the truth. And honesty is telling the truth to other people," says writer Spencer Johnson. By having complete candor, we will ultimately form healthier relationships with ourselves and others.

Can your partner count on you to tell them how you are really feeling? Can your colleagues know that you will follow through on your obligations? Do your friends anticipate that you will arrive at the time you promised? If the answer is no—imagine how you would feel if the situations were inverted. How would it be if your partner always hid their genuine emotions, your colleagues never completed tasks that they were assigned, or your friends chronically showed up two hours late? I imagine you would pull back—trust them increasingly less—until you finally vowed never to trust them again.

How often, in contrast, do we permit such behavior with ourselves? How often do we say, "I'll get to it tomorrow" and never do? How many of us say that it's "the last time I'll continue to flirt with that colleague," but then we have a key card for a hotel room in our sweaty hand? Have you conditioned yourself to accept falsehoods? Have you trained others to anticipate your lies or half-truths?

We need to achieve impeccability with our words through practice, risking vulnerability, and developing courage. We have to speak the truth even when it's hard, even when it's uncomfortable. We have to do what is right, even when it's not what's easiest. We have to appreciate that clear communication is ultimately more beneficial than convenience. At the same time, we have to keep in mind that striving for candor is not an excuse for being harsh, mean, or unkind. We should still endeavor to speak with compassion, even when offering uncomfortable information.

Many people avoid speaking honestly because they are afraid of hurting other people's feelings—but this seldom ends up being a valid justification for avoiding truthfulness. People are much more hurt by being misled, placated, or ignored. There is nothing wrong with saying, "There's a problem here, and we need to address it." When we come from a place of compassion and say, "I've made mistakes plenty of times—I know it doesn't feel good to realize when I've made one. You made a mistake here—and we need to fix it. There's no blame—

we just need to get it done." Such a response is ultimately much kinder than being misleading.

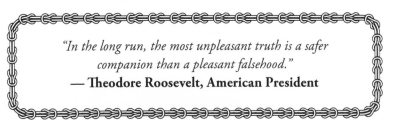

> *"In the long run, the most unpleasant truth is a safer companion than a pleasant falsehood."*
> — **Theodore Roosevelt, American President**

EXERCISE

For the next week, what would it feel like to speak only full truths? Would you be willing to give it a try? Remember that lying by omission is still lying, so be bold and share what you are really thinking. This exercise is not a hall pass giving you permission to insult or injure another person—but it'll be interesting to see how you navigate sticky situations with grace, bravery, and transparency.

At the end of the week, I would like for you to reflect on how you are feeling. Do you feel more at ease with yourself? Do you feel more integrated? Please journal about your experiences below.

In speaking my truth, I feel...

_____

_____

_____

_____

_____

_____

_____

_____

_____

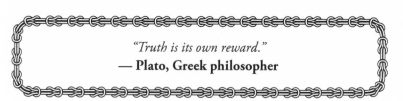

MEDITATION X

Close your eyes and imagine a reflection of yourself standing before you. Notice your height, your body shape. Notice yourself just as you are—strive to not change anything.

Now, I want you to smile at yourself and say, "We are going to be fully honest with ourselves. Is that okay?"

Watch and observe. Does your visualized self smile and nod—or do they look uncomfortable and glance to the side?

Ask your visualization to talk to you. How do they feel about being fully honest—to committing to living and speaking their truth? What feelings arise?

Listen and observe.

After some time, tell yourself that it'll be healthier to be more truthful. Though it may feel scary, they will ultimately feel so much more at ease, so much more confident if they fully embody their truth. Ask them what they will need in order to live in full honesty. What do they say?

You can stay in this meditation, conversing with yourself for as long as you need.

When you feel like you've reached a pausing point, invite yourself into your embrace—give yourself a hug. Tell yourself that you are beautiful, you are perfect just as you are, and that you are so brave.

Feel the visualized version of you merging with your own body.

Feel all of that commitment melt into you—infusing you with a desire to be more honest and more authentic.

Sit here, absorbing these feelings for as long as you need before coming back to yourself.

> "The doors to the world of the wild self are few but precious. If you have a deep scar, that is a door, if you have an old, old story, that is a door. [...] If you yearn for a deeper life, a full life, a sane life, that is a door."
> —**Clarissa Pinkola Estés, writer and psychoanalyst**

Expanding on the idea of choosing our words purposefully, we should pay attention to the narratives we share. When we tell a friend a story about the crazy events of our weekend, we bring into relief our own self-perceptions. When we tell a potential employer about our career trajectory, we reveal our personal values and motives. Any story with ourselves as the protagonist explains and clarifies who we believe ourselves to be.

Because of this, we must be conscientious about the sort of narratives we tell. They will ultimately become part of our psyches and integrated into our self-identities. Notice, what are the stories you tell—over and again—to represent your life? What are the tales you repeat over candlelit dinners and half-emptied bottles of wine? What excuses do you routinely share to make light of your shortcomings? These narratives may ultimately be connecting you with your innate identity or pulling you further away from it.

There is immense power inherent in the role stories play in our lives. We have been spinning tales since our ancestors were hunters and gatherers circling around cook fires. We swapped tales on how to trap, what plants to avoid, where the closest water sources ran clean.

Stories taught us skills, saved us from danger, and kept us alive. The reason stories feel so good to hear is that they share the same biological imperative as eating and sex—they ensure the survival of our species.

Stories are present from the earliest moments of childhood—parents weave together tales for us as they paraglide spoonfuls of mashed peas into our eagerly attentive maws. All the way from youthful choo-choo trains to adulthood and Jimmy Choos, we swap story arcs with our friends, lovers, caregivers, and collaborators. Stories flesh-out ideas, galvanize purpose, bond relationships, unify cohorts, inspire masses, and rationalize the chaotic happenings of our lives.

Through functional magnetic resonance imaging (fMRI), scientists have proven that when we listen to a story, the same areas in our own brains light up as in the storyteller's brain. For all intents and purposes, our minds make us feel as if we had experienced the events ourselves.[4] Stories kept us safe in the grasses of the Serengeti—and, similarly, stories give us tools to navigate the hazards of the modern world. We absorb other people's memories as our own and subsequently use them to thrive.

We, therefore, have to be careful about the stories with which we repeatedly engage. The more we hear or tell the same tale, the more robust neurological wiring we will create. As brain scientists say, "neurons that fire together, wire together"—meaning, that if we keep repeating the same thoughts, they will get strongly reinforced into our brain and become difficult to eradicate. If you tell a tale often enough, it will actually replace your first-hand memory of events. Therefore, if we continuously engage with stories of grief, heartache, and disillusionment—we will begin to sense that this is the truth of the world.

"I froze an incredibly formative experience at its trauma point," says comedian Hannah Gadsby, "and I sealed it off into jokes. And that story became a routine, and through repetition, that joke version fused with my actual memory of what happened. But, unfortunately, that joke version was not nearly sophisticated enough to help me undo the damage done to me." Her jokey retellings of her life experiences—because she repeated them onstage night after night—supplanted her actual memories and prevented her from fully healing.

Have you ever been to a family dinner where your uncle dives into an old tale about how he shot a hole-in-one at a renowned golf course—only to have your mother interrupt him and say, "That's not what happened! You've told that story so many times—and each time it gets further from the truth!" She goes on to explain how the original story concerned a doubles partner who got a birdie on a par-four. Then, the tale shifted to become the friend getting an eagle. Then it became a hole-in-one. Later, suddenly, your uncle became the one swinging the club. Disgruntled, your uncle shot back, "That isn't true! You don't remember at all." Stories rewrite memories.

So what are the stories that you've been telling about yourself? Again, any tale that is untruthful will ultimately pull you further away from your core, even if it is flattering. It is better to share things in as honest of a way as possible—neither self-aggrandizing nor self-humiliating—to the best of your abilities. Let things reveal their essence, while also realizing that we are never objective. We will forever have biases, personal perspectives, and opinions. We should strive to be as accountable to the truth as possible—while still holding the awareness that truth and fact may not be entirely aligned.

"The story — from Rumpelstiltskin to War and Peace — is one of the basic tools invented by the human mind for the purpose of understanding. There have been great societies that did not use the wheel, but there have been no societies that did not tell stories."
— **Ursula Le Guin, author**

EXERCISE

What are some of the core stories of your identity? We all have them—the narratives that speak to how we developed into the person we are now. They may include tales of our origin, our most harrowing moments, or the gut-twisting decisions that reverberate throughout our lives. For you, what are the most vibrant yarns that weave together to create the tapestry of your life?

The most important stories about me...

_____
_____
_____
_____
_____
_____
_____
_____
_____
_____
_____
_____
_____
_____
_____
_____
_____
_____
_____
_____
_____

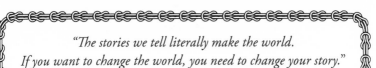

One thing we should do is re-evaluate our "quintessential tales," and see if we've outgrown them—see if they accurately reflect where we are right now. Stories become outdated rather quickly—we are no longer the same running back that we were when we won the homecoming game junior year of high school. We are no longer that awkward twenty-year-old, showing up for her first day at her new job, sweating and panting. Likewise, we are no longer the person we were even a week ago. If we are sharing stories that no longer reflect our current existence, they are going to feel misshapen and constrictive—like a shirt that shrunk in the dryer and is now three-sizes too small.

Especially since we've been on a growth expedition, exploring your personal *Journey to the Ecstatic Self*, you may be surprised to discover how certain narratives no longer resonate as true. We need to pick up each tale, one by one, and scrutinize it carefully. Perhaps some stories will need to be restructured, while others will need to be jettisoned. We will need to reconsider the key moments of our lives to find if they are aiding us on our current trajectory. There are countless moments from our history to choose from to highlight—are we picking the best ones to launch us skyward, or are we dwelling on anecdotes weighing us down?

What are the stories you want to be telling? Who is the person you want to be? Try to identify key moments in your life that are illustrative of the qualities you are coming to know yourself to possess. There may be previously unexamined experiences, thoughts, or happenings that slipped past your radar. Something may have seemed unimportant at the time that it occurred—but, upon later inspection, ended up being formative to the person you are now. Similarly, previously cherished memories can grow dull and prove inconsequential with the passage of time. Sometimes we have to let go of who we thought we were in order to blossom into the person we now understand ourselves to be.

It can be a daunting task to weave tales that are both comprehensive and compelling. We all love hearing well-told stories, but few of us think of ourselves as masterful storytellers. To become better narrators of the tales of our lives, we should look to the experts for guidance. Throughout your life, you have been attracted to specific films, books, television shows, plays, comic books, and video games because their stories resonated with you in some way. Perhaps you have a favorite novel that you come back to again and again—its pages all dog-eared and coffee-stained. Maybe there's a movie that you can recite line-by-line. Examine those narratives—there may be something in there that speaks to your spirit and can give you guidance as to the type of stories you ought to be telling about yourself.

For me, the *Harry Potter* series is endlessly entertaining. Why do these books mean so much to me? They resonate so much with my experiences as a young man. I recall how Harry longed to escape his wretched life under the stairs at the Dursleys'—and how that mirrored my own childhood, feeling trapped in a suffocated, internally disconnected life. Strange events happened around Harry that he couldn't understand—I remember instances in my own upbringing that felt similarly magical and inexplicable. Harry eventually learns that his life has greater worth than he previously believed—he learns to trust himself, cultivate courage, and value friendship. These are all skills that I, too, have fought hard to establish.

All stories steal from archetypes—quintessential plots that repeat over and over again. *Romeo and Juliet* is the same story as *West Side Story*, which is the same story as *The Fault in Our Stars*. *The Lion King* is a retelling of *Hamlet*. *The Odyssey* is also *The Lord of the Rings*, which is also *Raiders of the Lost Ark*. We can use these tropes to focus and refine our own stories. After all, if the overarching plot has been reused time and again, it is the details that make it feel fresh and new. Use a story archetype to build the underlying structure of your personal narrative—and bring in the specific happenings of your life to fill in the gaps. There are no new stories—there is only what newness you bring to them.

> "There is no such thing as a new idea. It is impossible. We simply take a lot of old ideas and put them into a sort of mental kaleidoscope. We give them a turn and they make new and curious combinations. We keep on turning and making new combinations indefinitely; but they are the same old pieces of colored glass that have been in use through all the ages."
>
> — **Mark Twain, American writer and philosopher**

EXERCISE

As I study how the *Harry Potter* story attracts me, I understand that there are key elements in its narrative that accurately map my own life. You can do the same by looking at the elements of the stories you know and love. What are archetypal stories for your journey? Perhaps the Andrea Sachs character in *The Devil Wears Prada* reminds you of how you gave up the glitz and glamour of a high-pressure world for a life that is more aligned with your values. Perhaps Luke Skywalker reminds you of how you were similarly able to move on from the tragedy of losing a parent-figure to a life of success in a noble field (hopefully as fulfilling to you as being an X-wing fighter and Jedi). We have stories that sing to us from the depths of bookshelves and inky blackness of screens—what are the siren tales calling out to you?

Archetypical Stories of My Life:

Title: _____

Character I most relate with: _____

_____

I connect with this story because: _____

222

_____
_____
_____
_____

Title: _____
Character I most relate with: _____

I connect with this story because: _____
_____
_____
_____

Title: _____
Character I most relate with: _____

I connect with this story because: _____
_____
_____
_____

Are there any commonalities between the stories you've listed above? If so, journal below.

_____
_____
_____
_____
_____
_____

> "Remember, this tradition comes to us not from the mists of Avalon, back in time, but further still—before we were scratching out these stories on papyrus, or we were doing the pictographs on walls in moist, damp caves. Back then, we had an urge, a need, to tell the story."
> — **Carmen Agra Deedee, storyteller and writer**

All stories are more or less the same. They begin by introducing a character whose life is fundamentally broken in some way. All protagonists are in desperate need of something (or are about to be)—otherwise, there'd be no story. If there was no strife, they'd just sit on their couch, happily eating potato chips. At some point near the beginning, something happens that makes them reconsider their life choices/outlook or upends life in some way. That change might be positive or negative—but they realize that they can no longer stay where they are. They set out on some kind of adventure, encounter a bunch of problems, face at least one crisis of faith, and eventually end up changed. Maybe they reach the goal they set out for—maybe they don't—but it doesn't matter. Over the course of the story, they learn something valuable about themselves in the process.

This is the framework onto which basically every story that has ever been told is laid. Fortunately for us, researchers have already identified the landmarks that come together that constitute a well-told story. They have flagged the critical moments of transition that a protagonist (and we, in our real lives) must go through to evolve. This quintessential story map has come to be known as "the hero's journey."

First described by literature professor Joseph Campbell, based on the work of psychologist Carl Jung, this "hero's tale" is mirrored in thousands of myths and legends throughout recorded history. Campbell's book, *The Hero with a Thousand Faces,* breaks down the stages a protagonist must go through into fifteen mystical plot points to achieve their goal. For our intents and purposes, I have streamlined this model into my own, simplified, nine-step version of a hero's quest. It can be a helpful guide when considering the moments in our personal narratives that have outsized importance/impact on our development.

The Archetypical Hero's Quest

The way things were. A hero starts out someplace, and usually, that place isn't so great. Luke is stranded on Tatooine, Harry is living under the stairs, Dorothy is trapped in Kansas. They know there's something more out there—but they're not sure how to get it.

The call of adventure. A mystical, robed figure shows up and tells the hero that their suspicions are correct—something more is out there for them to find. Sometimes that figure is a droid, sometimes they are a gamekeeper, sometimes they're a fortune teller. The main element is that the hero usually isn't ready to go yet—they'd prefer to hold onto the life they have rather than face the unknown.

The unbearable happens. *Well, shit.* Things didn't go quite as they hoped. A tornado touches down, whisks their house away, and suddenly they are forced to follow that call to adventure that they had thus far rejected. The protagonist gives up their known world and enters a place of mystery. In a lot of stories, this place of transformation is often a forest, a foreign country, or another planet. The point is, the hero has to give up comfort for growth.

Challenges arise. The hero is immediately tested. They realize that things aren't quite as cut and dry as they expected—life is more complicated than it appeared. Credos get challenged, perspectives get warped, and people begin to see that things aren't so clearly good/bad, black/white, benign/malevolent.

Things get worse. *Oh, no!* The road gets even steeper. Life is crushing the hero—but, like a piece of coal, the pressure is forming them into a diamond. Through struggle, hardship, and the overcoming of obstacles, the hero learns their worth, their purpose, and their real reason for existing.

A false victory. In a flash of light, the hero seemingly gets the thing they very much wanted. But it turns out to be a Pyrrhic victory—they realize that they had the wrong goal this whole time, or they have to sacrifice something that ultimately means more to them. They come to realize that a wish-granting gemstone can't grant happiness—riches cannot purchase what they really need. They recognize that they've been chasing a false illusion and refocus on attaining the thing that really matters most to them—often, it is their finding their innate truth or a sense of belonging.

Dark night of the soul. The hero enters a period of immense self-doubt—they fear that all is lost. They no longer know who they are, why they're fighting, or if they'll ever achieve lasting happiness. Their perspectives get inverted again—and they doubt if there will ever be a glimmer of light at the end of this unbearably long tunnel.

Final climax. The hero—who is now battered and bruised beyond recognition—emerges from the pit of self-doubt to slay the dragon, kill the witch, and confront their inner demons. Because they learned so much about themselves in the pit of despair, they now have the skills to be victorious. They murder the beast, win the gold, and rescue the hapless prisoners. But, more importantly, they have saved themselves. They realize that they are the heroes of their own narratives.

Return home. Life settles into a new normal. Perhaps the hero returns to the place they once called home only to discover that it no longer feels the same. Maybe they build a new life, realizing that they can never go back to their unenlightened existences. Regardless, they have come full circle. The adventure is now over (at least temporarily—until the next installment), and they are forever changed. It is important to note that they can never *truly* go home again—they are an entirely different person because of the adventure they went on. Now that they know their worth, they will never accept the lesser life that they used to have.

Whew! Epic, isn't it? Can you recognize many of your favorite plots encapsulated in this one tale? Of course, there are exceptions—but *so many* stories follow this general outline.

I want you to examine your journey of moving into wholeness—of finding intrinsic happiness and self—and see if you can graph it onto this story-structure. It may not be an exact fit—you may need to tweak or trim things here and there—but it is a good starting point. Remember that this is your tale, and you can tell it any way you would like. Facts can be represented in a variety of ways—all while still remaining truthful. Take, for example, this very brief depiction of my life—told from three different vantages. I could spin my threads in a variety of ways—all of them equally honest. The difference lies in the story I want to tell and what I believe myself to be.

Story of My Life: Version 1

I grew up awkward. I never felt at home within my skin nor within the world I was told to call my home. Most people laughed at me—called me names like "weirdo," "sissy," or "fag." By the time I graduated from college, I had entirely disassociated from myself. I was living a lie in regard to my sexuality and hyper-masculine gender performance—and I was miserable. I was pursuing a career as an actor, which I hoped would become a surrogate in providing feelings of validation—but it did not.

It has been a lifetime of struggle, heartbreak, and constant reorientation in order to identify my true self. I have fought hard to know who I am, what I want, and what I need. While I am much happier and well-adjusted than I used to be, it has been such a steep climb up a craggy canyon cliff of self-doubt that I am now exhausted. I sometimes feel like I need a twenty-year nap to fully recuperate from the hard lessons I've endured.

Well, that's one option. Not necessarily the most cheery one, is it? I imagine if that was the tale I told day in and day out, I'd find myself feeling depressed and melancholy. Not that this is necessarily a *bad* story...it's just not the story I would like to ingrain into my mind. Let's try again...

Story of My Life: Version 2

Some might posit that I came from a distant planet—that I am an alien, of sorts. As a child, I had wild, kaleidoscopic insights about people and events that exceeded rational thought. My musings were reflective of an old spirit rather than a young whippersnapper. I remember sitting on the side of the playground, watching my peers scuttle about with balls and jump ropes, while I pondered existential questions about the purpose of being.

My life has since been a consistent journey of studying the deeper meaning of my existence. From moving into a spiritual refuge, to exploring the consciousness-querying career of an actor, I have devoted my life to self-understanding. I felt like such an outsider through my upbringing— but that outsider status drove me to understand the inner workings of the mind in a uniquely profound way. Today, I am happy to coach others on their journey toward wholeness and self-acceptance.

Alright, well, that one certainly highlights my outsider status. But I also sound a tad bit nutty. I am not sure that's the sort of tale I'd want to share with my friends and relatives—or had read aloud to a group before I walked onstage to work with them. It is, however, an entirely valid option and one that truthfully represents my experiences.

Here's one more go...

Story of My Life: Version 3

From the time I was very young, I wanted to be a professional actor. Other kids thought I was weird for wanting to role-play and plan out elaborate scenes—they mainly wanted to toss hacky sacks and swap gossip. I devoted my teenage years and young adulthood to becoming a formidable actor—sacrificing time with loved ones and sleep to attain the skills I needed. The interesting thing is, once I was on the cusp of reaching my goals (living in LA, booking lots of work, with a creative team supporting me), I realized that everything that had driven me to that moment had actually been the goal in and of itself. Everything I had learned up to that point had taught me that I no longer needed to be a successful actor—I was happy enough just being me. I ended up moving across the country to be with my fiancé and building a life based on full-hearted, non-scripted interactions. I am now happier than I ever was. Plus, my worth is no longer dependent on a headline splayed across an electric marquis.

That one is probably better. The truth is, there are as many ways of spinning my life's tale as there are words in the dictionary. I just need to find the one that feels most aligned with me at this point in time.

Who is the person you want to be? Have you been telling the narrative of your life from a negative perspective for too long—dimming the light of your brilliance, burying your goodness under the dust of unworthiness? I encourage you to be bold, to be heroic, to follow this quest. My example stories are much shorter than yours is going to be—but many of the essential points are still there.

I also encourage you to steer away from the "victim narrative." Yes, bad things happen to us. Yes, tragedy strikes, and we feel powerless to make a difference. But if your stories are all about other people doing hurtful things to you, then you are giving up your personal power. You are losing your status as "hero" and putting that crown on another person. Good stories are not told about the poor people to which shitty things happen—they are told about the remarkable people who overcame adversity.

How were you able to spin the hay into gold? How were you able to burn the dross that life gave you to power a steamboat and carry you away? I am not advocating avoiding or denying the trauma you faced—I am merely suggesting that you get to write the tale and, therefore, the ending. You are not a victim. You have the power, the agency to control the narrative. If you own your story—then you have the ability to choose how and where it ends.

> *"In life, there are no essentially major or minor characters.*
> *To that extent, all fiction and biography, and most historiography,*
> *are a lie. Everyone is necessarily the hero of his own life story.*
> *Hamlet could be told from Polonius's point of view and called*
> *The Tragedy of Polonius, Lord Chamberlain of Denmark.*
> *He didn't think he was a minor character in anything, I daresay."*
> **—John Barth, writer**

EXERCISE

The heralds are blaring their horns, announcing the arrival of your epic tale. Going through the hero's journey that I described above, how can you tell the story of how you became the integrated, self-aware, and altogether awesome person that you are (or are evolving into being)? Take your time; it may take a few iterations to work this out.

The Way Things Were _____

_____

_____

_____

_____

The Call of Adventure _____

_____

_____

_____

_____

The Unbearable Happens _____

_____

_____

_____

_____

Challenges Arise _____

_____

_____

Things Get Worse _____

_____

_____

_____

A False Victory _____

_____

_____

_____

Dark Night of the Soul _____

_____

_____

_____

Final Climax _____

_____

_____

_____

Return Home _____

_____

_____

_____

_____

And then, tying this all together—what is the major theme or lesson that was learned? If you had to boil your story down to a single anecdote, moral, or idea—what would it be?

The Moral of My Story _____

_____

_____

_____

_____

> *"It's like everyone tells a story about themselves inside their own head. Always. All the time. That story makes you what you are. We build ourselves out of that story."*
> **—Patrick Rothfuss, writer**

You need to claim ownership over your story—don't let anyone else take it away from you. If you firmly believe that the story you've chosen best encapsulates who you really are, don't let any parent, authority figure, or friend steal it away. It may take time for other people's perception of you to reconcile with your own, consciously-chosen vantage. But, in time, they will learn. As we grow and evolve, others tend to want to see us as being the person they always knew us to be. It can be challenging and frustrating to teach our loved ones to see us in a new light. But they have to. They ultimately have to accept us for who we really are.

I would like to add a few words of caution here regarding the sacredness of your story. Don't compare it with another person's. Your story is special—no one has lived the life you have. They don't know your struggles, your hardships, and what you sacrificed to get where you are. By comparing your tale to theirs—you cheapen the lessons you've learned. You don't want to feel like your story lacks significance by measuring it against another's. Yours is beautiful and whole, just as it is on its own.

Given the age of social media in which we live, it is easy to see someone else's seemingly gleaming life and feel like ours is insufficient. Never believe this! Please, yes, read about and study those individuals who inspire you—but don't compare. If you do, you may forever feel inadequate.

Your story is beautiful and worth sharing. Don't let other people tell you otherwise—or make you believe that their stories about your life are more important/accurate than your own. You have a story that needs to be heard—and no one can tell it like you can. Shout it from the mountaintops. Celebrate the value of everyone's tale—but simultaneously hold your own as precious. It is your life, after all.

EXERCISE

A great way to tune out other people's stories and hone in on our own is to take a social media break. I know it can be frightening to imagine, but it actually can be very beneficial. Consider going online and deactivating each of your social media profiles for at least a week. You don't need to let everyone know you're doing it—they don't really care all that much anyway. Anyone you need to talk to will be able to find you via phone, text message, paper post, or in person. Surrender this fear of missing out and lean into the realization that actual life is much more interesting than its digital reflection.

This may cause anxiety, I know. But try it. Really, what have you got to lose? It'll still be there waiting for you if you decide that you're better off engaging once your tech detox is complete.

I am taking a social media break from _____ until
_____ dates.

My friend, named _____, is holding me accountable, because I know I'll be challenged to actually stay logged-off.

If you want to take this one step further, perhaps even consider going entirely screen-free for a number of days to truly unplug. That is—only if you're feeling truly wild.

In its place, dream up a list of people whose stories you'd like to imbibe. Who are the heroes by whom you'd like to be inspired? Download, purchase, or borrow some books/documentaries chronicling their lives and struggles. Learn from the greats—steal lessons from them.

Documentaries/Biographies with which I'd like to engage:

_____
_____
_____
_____
_____
_____

> *"When writing the story of your life, don't let somebody else hold the pen."*
> **—Harley Davidson, motorcycle company**

By focusing on narratives of resilience, of our innate ability to thrive and overcome defeat, we cultivate grit. We become individuals who are able to transmute hardship into growth-filled lessons. By reframing our struggles as mere steps on a longer journey of coming into wholeness, we crown ourselves victors. We become those who overcame the odds, succeeded despite the deck being stacked against them. A well-told story can turn us from stable boys into heroes, from orphans into wizards, and from street urchins into queens. Our stories gift us with the power of resilience, an understanding that our current discomfort is but one chapter of a much longer book.

Perspective is everything. And when you consciously choose your stories, you get to choose the vantage through which they're told. You get to pick the lens. You get to decide when it's time to set down the pen.

SUMMARY:

— **Words have power. Be conscientious of the words you use to describe yourself. Let your words be honest.**

— **Stories create memory—they help us refine our identity.**

— **We choose the focus of the story. We need to believe that we are the hero, that our tale is worth telling, and that we are worthy of being heard.**

Chapter 9:

CRUMBLING PATHS UNDERFOOT

"Sometimes the most painful lesson we can learn is that certain things are not meant to be. We can give it our best shot, change everything about ourselves, be persistent, pray to a higher power, and so on, but we still don't reach the result we desire. [...] Those who focus only on finishing first can sometimes miss the lesson of the race: who we become in the pursuit of the goal."
—Char Margolis, spiritual intuitive and television host

As we internally grow and mature, our priorities change. At one time, becoming a famous actor, developing a cover-model-worthy body, and marrying a brilliant woman mattered a great deal to me. But as I learned about myself and grew into my being—I had to shift my priorities. I abandoned my career in the entertainment industry because it no longer fit my life goals. I cultivated appreciation for my body as it is without hormonal supplementation. I married a man who electrifies my soul. But there are still times when wistful longing takes hold, and I reminisce about the dreams I have abandoned. Those cherished memories that I jettisoned in pursuit of the self.

I am deeply satisfied with where I am in my life—but, even so, I still sometimes mourn the lives I might have lived. What would have happened if I'd stayed in Los Angeles and toughed it out longer? What if the first person I fell in love with hadn't dumped me—what if he had suddenly becomemore emotionally aware and able to communicate his feelings? What if I had accepted that young, Swedish woman-I-met-aboard-a-flight-to-Europe's offer to abandon my study abroad plans so I could backpack with her around Northern Africa?

Even if I could go back in time to advise my younger self, I probably wouldn't change anything. I have no regrets regarding the paths that I have picked. But there are still days when melancholy wraps me in its soggy embrace. There are times when I wonder if I could have become a different person. Is there an alternative version of me existing out there in the folds of a parallel universe?

As you are in the midst of this book (and presumably the throes of your own coming-into-wholeness journey), I suspect you're envisioning a lot of different potentials for your life—different ways it could manifest. I bet you are also beginning to recognize that some of the dreams you've held and worked decades to realize won't actually be in your best interest. You may be coming to terms with the fact that you might never have the life you fervently sought. And with that admittance will come grief.

There will likely be a phase where you will have to mourn the death of your plans and imaginings. The flavor of the emotion may vary—you could experience anger, indignation, lethargy, rage, a sense of betrayal. What's under each of these feelings, however, is a disappointment in ourselves. Why couldn't I have done differently? Why didn't I try harder? Why couldn't I have seen the warning signs before I wasted years of my life? Why was I so self-deluded? Could I still get those things I wanted, even if they're not meant for me? Who am I if I am not the person that I thought I was? If I no longer have that job/title/career/spouse/car to define me, what can I call "me?"

When we turn away from the path we envisioned—and probably mood-boarded, collaged, and journaled about—it can feel shattering. I know, for me, accepting that I would never have the destiny I coveted made my sense of self crumble. I no longer knew how to navigate in the world, explain who I was, or articulate what I do. There were days spent huddling under covers and listlessly staring out of windows. I searched the clouds for omens that would direct me where to head next. I felt hapless and aimless.

Further, trying to bury, hide, or dilute the uncomfortable emotions didn't make the reintegration process complete itself any quicker. Trying to ignore my feelings did not make me any closer to being whole again. In fact, the opposite was true. Trying to distance myself from the discomfort only drew out my agony. I had to learn to face the pain head-on. By leaning into the "suck"—embracing the uncertainty, the unknown, the uncomfortable—healing increased. By allowing myself to muck about in the mud, fumble through the loss and bewilderment, a route forward became more discernible.

I suspect that, with each iteration of world-dissolution, we develop better coping skills for processing the chaos. For me, early disappointments prepared me for the later, more significant heartbreaks in my future. With each passing storm, I became more adept at enduring, more resilient. Not only that, but I have also gained a profound trust in myself. By surviving the unimaginable, I have learned to trust in my grit—my tenacity to endure.

Once your desires have been stripped away—once the illusions of your life have been ripped apart—what remains will never be able to be taken from you. You will know your essence by knowing grief. Once you've survived the ending of your imagined world, you will know yourself. Your ability to endure will eventually become your strength and the source of your power.

What are the areas in your life that you realize are no longer serving you? There maybe have been things you've invested in, trials you've hoped to win, gauntlets that you've fought to complete—but do they still matter? Many of us make life decisions based on what we think will bring us the greatest happiness at that time—but as we mature and our perspectives change, we realize that we need something more, better, or just altogether different.

It can be heartbreaking to realize that your spouse, your job, or your neighborhood no longer support your current vantages. Hopefully, you've been open about your discoveries along the way—inviting the people who matter to grow with you. But, sometimes, this is not the case. It is totally fine to realize (about someone or some situation) that: "I love them, we have had fantastic experiences, but I need something different." It can be devastating to acknowledge—but until you can face it, it'll be challenging to move on and be able to heal. If where you are right now is not conducive to your evolution, to you coming into your wholeness, then these circumstances may need to be addressed.

Be sure that you tread lightly. We have made agreements with our loved ones, and it is essential that we honor them. While self-exploration is important, we have to be conscious of minimizing harm to others in the process. Try not to burn bridges—we may need to re-tread them in the future. Do not abandon individuals who depend on you. Be kind and be respectful to others as you work to come into your truth.

Your path forward will become clearer once you understand where you are standing. If you can name your current whereabouts, where you know you shouldn't or can't go, and where you think you need to head, it'll be easier to walk onward. So take your time, journal about this, and make sure you're settled on a course before you make irreparable declarations. Clarity comes over time—avoid being rash and blowing up critical safety networks on a whim. You are responsible to others beyond yourself—be compassionate and kind.

Life Plans That I am Grieving:

_____

_____

_____

_____

_____

_____

_____

_____

_____

_____

_____

> "We live in a fantasy world, a world of illusion.
> The great task in life is to find reality."
> — **Iris Murdoch, British novelist and philosopher**

I would like to share with you a story about an instance where my world unraveled—when I had to reckon with the fact that what I'd always imagined for my life was not my reality.

A few months before my twenty-eighth birthday, I faced a life-altering decision: stay in Hollywood and continue to pursue my career as an actor—or move back to Chicago, settle in with my fiancé, and reorient my life toward intrinsic values. I had been living in Los Angeles for five months—and was feeling successful. I had won entrée into elite acting groups, garnered a team of managers and agents to represent me, and booked several worthwhile projects. By all accounts,

I was thriving as a performer new to Tinsel Town. My peers were applauding my successes, and I felt like my years of striving were finally coming to fruition.

But something wasn't right—a knot in my belly recognized that I wasn't fully aligned with my deeper values. I sensed that my continuing to pursue this line of work would ultimately pull me away from the qualities that I believed would give me lasting happiness and fulfillment. I remember one moment in particular when I sat down for a private one-on-one with a prestigious talent agent. He wasn't looking at representing me at that time, but he agreed to have a frank discussion about my goals and career trajectory. As we talked, he brought some truths into harsh relief.

He said, "Kae, you can have all this. You can be famous; you can be successful—but it's going to take around ten years and every drop of focus you can muster. You won't be able to maintain friendships or keep a long-term partner—you won't have time for them. This is going to demand everything you have. If you give it your all—when you're around thirty-eight—you might have it: the golden ring. The awards and glamour that everyone chases. Are you willing to trade in the other parts of your life for these accolades? Because that is what is going to be required for you to succeed."

I had no words to reply. But in my heart, I knew that it was not a sacrifice I was willing to make. I wouldn't trade in my intrinsic well-being for glitz and trophies. I wanted substance. I wanted a full life. I longed to be truly happy—and I understood that Hollywood wouldn't give me any of that.

But this realization was in direct opposition to everything I had promised my younger self. All the aspirations I had carved into my spirit when I was a young man demanded that I attain these cinematic laurels, no matter the personal cost. The desires that I cultivated as a teenager—longing to be Batman—fought back against my burgeoning self-awareness.

My mind searched back to the colleagues I'd met who had attained some level of notoriety in Los Angeles. I reflected on how—in every conversation, at every event—they were treated as commodities.

People always sized them up by how much money they could bring in, how big of an audience, how much luster they could provide. What was their worth? How much juice could be squeezed out of them?

I didn't want to feel like a piece of produce. I didn't want to look back on my life at the age of seventy or so and say, "Wow! I won an Oscar. I was a superhero. But I gave up the things that really mattered. I no longer have real friends or family I'm close to. I used to have a partner who cherished me—but I traded him in for accolades." I was afraid that I would realize that I'd made an enormous mistake.

Even though it terrified me—even though it went against the years I had spent actively pursuing the goal—I called my fiancé and told him I was leaving Hollywood. I loaded up my Fiat and drove back home to Chicago. Ironically enough, I had to park my car at the Denver airport and fly back to Los Angeles because I learned—mid-road trip—that I had booked yet another commercial and was required for a costume fitting the following day. Shoot completed, I flew back to Denver, hopped into my car, and have (mostly) never looked back.

Sure, there are times where I wonder what life would have been like if I'd made different choices regarding my career—but, honestly, I couldn't imagine being happier. Not once during my time in Hollywood did I meet someone that made me feel genuinely inspired. Not once did I encounter an individual and think, "Wow! I long to live your life—I want to be you." No matter how successful, no matter how illustrious, there was no one that possessed an aura that I longed to adopt for myself. It felt frightening to turn my back on my decades-long desires; but, ultimately, I had to admit that they were no longer aligned with my more mature self-understanding. I wanted more than fame and riches. I craved a genuinely satisfying life—and if tabloids teach us anything, most celebrities are far from contented.

After I got home and settled back into Midwestern life, I became disoriented and depressed. I had spent the previous decade-plus striving to attain a specific goal. Becoming a legendary actor had been at the forefront of every decision I made, every meal that I ate, and every trip to the gym. Once that was no longer at the center of my thoughts, I didn't know what to do. Life had lost its purpose and meaning. I felt like a boat drifting, severed from its moorings. Life seemed flat. What was the point of working out if it wasn't for a photoshoot? Why should I bother reading books if it wasn't for deepening my understanding of a character? I had to begin dreaming up new possible scenarios for my life—I had to recalibrate my compass.

I wish I could say that it was a fairly swift, painless transition—that I identified new horizons and effortlessly adjusted my course. But the truth of the matter is that it took years for my sense of self to settle. I had to remeasure my creativity; I had to chart my artistic spirit anew. I knew that I wanted to be brave, to be authentic—but I had no clear direction in which to head. To make matters worse, a second great storm was on the horizon, about to break. Soon, another surge of identity-destroying chaos would send my sense of emotional bearings reeling.

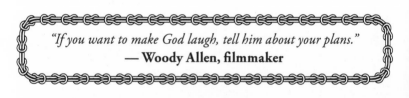

"If you want to make God laugh, tell him about your plans."
— **Woody Allen, filmmaker**

MEDITATION XI

Find a comfortable seat and feel your body turn into jelly. Let your muscles, your tendons, your fascia relax. Become supple, inert, bendy. Allow yourself to release whatever it is you're holding. Deeply let go.

It's time to channel your inner Disney princess—you know the one to which I am alluding. Imagine yourself standing tall on the edge of a frosty mountain, shouting to the wind, "Let it go." Let everything go. Your hopes, your desires, your preferred outcomes. Relax into what is. Let go of what you hoped to attain—surrender to what is possible.

Feel yourself release. Drop. Give in. Give up. There is nothing but the present—nothing but what is. Be here now.

And mourn, if you need to. Cry. Bemoan. Holler to the high heavens. If it is helpful—allow yourself to grieve. It is perfectly alright to feel whatever is coming up for you. It's okay to be disappointed. It's okay to experience loss. We need to accept our sorrow in order to fully live again.

Sit with your sense of release, your sense of loss. Be at peace with your grief. Allow it to exist—don't shut it out.

You are where you are—and where you are is perfect.

Stay here for as long as you need. Howl into this wind, if you require. Beat a drum. Express your disappointment.

As we discern our path forward, we should focus on two ideas. First, allowing our life plans to be less like roadmaps and more like arrows on a compass. A map shows a fixed destination and a defined route to get there. A compass, by contrast, points in a direction in which to go. Coming into wholeness and living our most integrated life is a constantly evolving internal discussion. Each time you name a goal and start working toward it, you will find that life will nudge your plans in a different trajectory than expected. I know that I might dream up a specific project to accomplish—but by the time it is completed, it'll have gone through thirty iterations. It will be quite different than I initially imagined. Often, life takes on forms that are far beyond what we supposed or anticipated.

If we stay too rigidly fixated on a specific outcome, we miss the omens life provides to bring us into alignment. We need to be flexible, adaptable, and willing to update our coordinates based on the most current information. We must view our plans as being beacons pointing us in the right direction, but leave space for adventure and surprises to adjust the course along the way. I encourage you to dream up what a more self-realized vision of what life will look like, but be very open about how it manifests.

Listen to your intuition, and pay attention to the subtle hints in the world around you. I find that the right guidance comes at the exact moments I most need it—from eavesdropped conversations, a surprisingly timely news article, or a friend randomly offering the precise piece of information I need to hear. The plans I had at the beginning of any endeavor are never complete—I am ever learning and filling in the blanks as I go.

As you deal with grieving your abandoned hopes and dreams, give yourself something to be moving toward—new shining lights to focus on. We have so much invested in our identities, in our previous relationships, in our plans for the future. To let them go—even if we consciously know we no longer want them—can be devastating. You will likely go through an intense period of mourning. I certainly have. Having something proactive to fixate on can be beneficial. With this in mind, let's do a little dreaming up of what might supplant that which we are in the process of losing.

EXERCISE

To aid us in gaining better awareness around the areas of our lives that are enriching us versus hindering us, we should chart our energy levels throughout the day. When are the moments where we are feeling invigorated? How about when we are feeling drained?

In the space below, list the most common activities/relationships/events in your life—and, beside them, rank how much energy they either take or give. If it is a neutral influence, mark it in the middle. If it's highly positive, mark a space somewhere to the right—if negative, to the left.

Think of yourself as being a battery in a hybrid car—you are being either charged or emptied with each action you undertake. We only have so much life force, and we ideally want to be engaged with people and activities that fill us up. The items you list can include people, habits, practices, activities—anything that you interact with regularly.

(-)Empty - - - - - - - - - - | - - - - - - - - - Full(+)

(-)Empty - - - - - - - - - - | - - - - - - - - - Full(+)

(-)Empty - - - - - - - - - - | - - - - - - - - - Full(+)

(-)Empty - - - - - - - - - - | - - - - - - - - - Full(+)

(-)Empty - - - - - - - - - - | - - - - - - - - - Full(+)

(-)Empty - - - - - - - - - - | - - - - - - - - - Full(+)

(-)Empty - - - - - - - - - - | - - - - - - - - - Full(+)

(-)Empty - - - - - - - - - - | - - - - - - - - - Full(+)

(-)Empty - - - - - - - - - - | - - - - - - - - - Full(+)

(-)Empty - - - - - - - - - - | - - - - - - - - - Full(+)

(-)Empty - - - - - - - - - - | - - - - - - - - - Full(+)

(-)Empty - - - - - - - - - - | - - - - - - - - - Full(+)

(-)Empty - - - - - - - - - - | - - - - - - - - - Full(+)

(-)Empty - - - - - - - - - - | - - - - - - - - - Full(+)

(-)Empty - - - - - - - - - - | - - - - - - - - - Full(+)

(-)Empty - - - - - - - - - - | - - - - - - - - - Full(+)

(-)Empty - - - - - - - - - - | - - - - - - - - - Full(+)

(-)Empty - - - - - - - - - - | - - - - - - - - - Full(+)

What do you notice about your responses? What are your life-force filler-uppers? What are your energy drains? What is the ratio between the two—how much of what you are doing adds to your life-force versus takes away from it? How could you cultivate more of the energy-giving elements? Journal about your observations below.

My Life-Force Battery:

_____
_____
_____
_____
_____
_____
_____
_____
_____
_____

"The world doesn't need more successful people, the world desperately needs more peacemakers, healers, rebuilders, storytellers and lovers of every type."
—**His Holiness, the 14th Dalai Lama, spiritual leader**

Based on the exercise you did prior, you may have some ideas regarding the areas that are feeding your spirit. What would it look like to design your life around these life-giving elements?

I would like to invite you to dream up three possible scenarios for your future. Take time to think outside the box. What if you reimagined some of those life plans that you packed away in a trunk under your bed? What if you started a new career—one thoroughly aligned with your mission and your interests? What if you gave everything up and grabbed an old-timey camera, a few rolls of film, and an around-the-world plane ticket that allows you to stop anywhere, so long as you keep heading east? What are some "dream" lives that you've put "on hold?"

Life Idea 1

_____
_____
_____
_____
_____

Life Idea 2

_____
_____
_____
_____

Life Idea 3

_____
_____
_____

_____

_____

Life Idea 4

_____

_____

_____

_____

_____

Reread what you wrote and notice the ways each idea continues to resonate within you. We can take this dreaming a step further by seeing how these ideas align with your values and abilities.

On a scale of one (low) to ten (high), how well does each life idea connect with your enhanced self-understanding? Do they feel mission and vision aligned? Do you think they would enrich the life of the "real" you?

Intrinsic Alignment of Each Life Idea

1. _____ 2. _____ 3. _____ 4. _____

Still ranking from one to ten, how likely does it seem that you could actually make each dream a reality? Is there really a possibility that you could make each one work, practicality considered? We all have commitments and laws of physics that we must honor—while still challenging ourselves to seek the unexpected. I'm never going to be an aerospace engineer for NASA—and I have to be okay with that because it's beyond the scope of what is attainable with the years I have left in life.

Feasibility of Each Life Idea

1. _____ 2. _____ 3. _____ 4. _____

Do you think that each life plan would make you lastingly happy? Sure, selling all your possessions and living as an itinerant writer in Bali might be fun for a short time—but do you really want to make that your *whole* life? You want to pick trajectories that you'll relish for decades, not just weeks. Rank a plan as low if it comes across as being only a quick burst of happiness—high if it seems enjoyable for the long-term.

Lasting Satisfaction for Each Life Idea

1. _____ 2. _____ 3. _____ 4. _____

Do you have the skills and/or talents required to make a plan work? You absolutely can enroll in a training program, go back to school, or apprentice with a seasoned professional—but do you have the requisite abilities to do the craft? If your dream life is becoming a headlining soprano at the Metropolitan Opera, but you can barely keep a tune to "Merrily We Row Along," you probably aren't going to be hired to belt out the high notes center stage. Be reasonable in regard to your abilities and the amount of study and time required to master a new skill.

Requisite Skill Level for Each Life Idea

1. _____ 2. _____ 3. _____ 4. _____

We enter relationships, hobbies, or clubs with the assumption that we will enjoy engaging with them for a very long time—but, often, we end up feeling bored and burned out after just a short while. Is this a life plan that you will be able to sustain? Do you have the stamina to build momentum and keep the life plan aloft for (hopefully) decades? Or will you peter out? I may desire to found a billion-dollar tech start-up; but if I can't handle sleeping at my desk for four years and never seeing my family, I might not have the energetic resources to see it through. You don't want to give up on a plan partway through because your battery has run dry.

Ability to Sustain the Energy Required for Each Life Idea

1. _____ 2. _____ 3. _____ 4. _____

Go through and decide which of the four scenarios you created had the highest overall marks. Perhaps you could hybridize two of the Life Plans to create an optimized one? Describe a possible hybridized Life Plan below that draws on the best of each. Again, this is not road-mapping—this is just active dreaming regarding directions you may want to head.

My Ideal Life (based on my values):

_____
_____
_____
_____
_____
_____
_____
_____

What would a five-year plan look like for this life? Go ahead and plot it out in the space below.

Year one: _____
_____
_____
_____

Year two: _____
_____
_____
_____
_____

Year three: _____
_____

_____

_____

_____

Year four: _____

_____

_____

_____

Year five: _____

_____

_____

_____

_____

What do you see as being the first few steps required to develop this idea into reality?

To make this intrinsically-aligned vision of my life a reality, I will need to do the following:

1. _____

_____

2. _____

_____

3. _____

_____

4. _____

_____

_____

Sometimes our lives change due to an active decision—a choice to pursue a new path. We realize that we are not living a life aligned with our values, our heightened understanding of ourselves, and we purposefully course-correct. But not all plans shift due to our own volition. Sometimes our ambitions and dreams face existential peril due to forces outside of our control. If a tornado comes, picks up our house, and carries us to a distant land of munchkins, rainbows, and silver slippers—suddenly, our plans for Kansas have to be abandoned.

I'd like to share the story of a second storm that came and demolished my plans for the future—one that arose shortly after I touched down back in the Midwest, still reeling from the chaos of leaving California. This one arose from leaving the ashram—it was a hurricane that I never saw coming. After it departed, however, I realized that the devastation it wrought was precisely what I needed for my next level of growth. Without the pain and tumult, I wouldn't have fully matured.

I had been a part of the ashram and its related spiritual community for over eight years. I had learned much about spirituality and my deeper self, grown as a person, and established roots into soulful understanding. I discovered a feeling of home and belonging in a robust way, unlike anything I'd experienced prior. I felt intrinsically linked with the people, their mission, and the teachings.

I intended and planned to remain part of that meditative tradition for the entirety of my life—I aspired to rise within its ranks to become a senior teacher and guardian of the *dharma*. I spent all of my spare time, money, and resources to help it thrive—I devoted my whole self to its success.

Despite—or perhaps precisely because of—my intense state of devotion to this tradition, I couldn't see how I was being abused. I missed how I was being psychologically manipulated and stunted in many areas. I was asked (and willingly gave) all my personal power over to the head teacher, the "guru." He changed my name, told me what I could eat, where I could live, when I could travel. He dictated whether aspirants could have children, see their families, or work outside of the community—and, if so, what sort of occupation they should pursue. He was someone who could not be questioned, challenged, or replaced. He was, after all, "perfected."

I should have seen the warning signs.

I was nineteen when I met him. I was young, impressionable, and incredibly lonely. I was disconnected from meaningful community, awkward, and ostracized from my peer group at college. I was afraid of my human longings and wanted to feel exceptional and special. I was exactly the sort of person who was ripe for plucking to join a cult.

By giving away my personal volition, I was supposed to receive the "grace of the guru." A mystical power that would eventually turn me into an enlightened bodhisattva. So long as I did everything that he said, I would become a perfected human living on Earth. The guru, in return, vowed to do whatever it took to help me achieve that state— even if it took many lifetimes of reincarnating with me to help me attain liberation.

I bet you can see where this is going better than I could at that time.

The relationship was not healthy. Sure, I experienced many moments of intense love and celebrating life while part of the ashram. But there were also moments of horrible physical and emotional abuse that I witnessed first-hand and dismissed because it was just "the teacher's grace." I was told that lashing out at a devotee was part of the process of breaking down their "ego"—their limited sense of self. I forgave senior leaders who hurt me and others because that was what I was indoctrinated to do. I became fanatical, a zealot. It played well into my desire to be anything but ordinary—to escape my humanness. I wore my suffering as a badge of honor.

Fortunately, life had other plans for me besides remaining with them. Thanks largely to my sexual coming out and exploration of my orientation, I cultivated a growing sense of selfhood. I matured into myself in a well-rounded way and established stronger personal boundaries that brought with them the notion of self-respect. A person who was in the process of becoming whole did not fit into the power-structure maintained by this spiritual tradition—we were meant to remain in a limited, child-like state.

I also discovered that I had robust meditative abilities. I could lead people. I could speak well and communicate ideas thoughtfully. All of this made me dangerous—I could threaten the existing hierarchy. As I became more enthusiastically myself, I also became a liability. I understood that I didn't need the "teacher" to grow spirituality in the same way other devotees professed they did—I believed that people could trust their own judgment. I pierced the veil of the tradition's manipulative narrative—and this made it necessary for me to be ex-communicated.

I do want to be fair; there were beautiful, genuine teachings as part of this tradition. There were magnificent truths, gorgeous fellow devotees, and fantastical sensations of cosmic oneness. There was a real sense of spiritual connection, rich tradition, and heart-fluttering inspiration woven into my time there. But there was also darkness. There was mental instability amongst its leaders—and there were lies perpetuated to ensure compliance with the prescribed order. Practitioners were kept in states of perpetual fear, of destabilization, so the only fixed point on which to latch was the guru at the forefront. He was the one constant.

That guru became a Christ figure—an irreplaceable savior. My relationship with him felt like a sacred bond—something that would be there for me to count on for the rest of my days, in this world or the next. Even with my awakening, I still planned for the rest of my life to be connected with him and his ashram.

Imagine my surprise when, one morning, I received a barrage of angry text messages and emails from him and his wife accusing me of heinous acts. Flat out lies. I had stood up on behalf of someone involved in the community who was being targeted with slander, gaslighting, and acts of hatred. It was too much for the teacher and his wife—my assertiveness. The guru issued a pronouncement that I was no longer a part of their tradition and told everyone in the community that I'd gone insane. I was thrown out of their faith tradition and was instructed to never contact him or anyone else in the ashram ever again. They demanded that my friends treat me like a pariah. In the course of one morning, I lost a vast swath of my identity.

I was shaken. No, I was shattered. I was broken into a million, tiny pieces. My many plans for my future with this spiritual tradition crumbled into dust, along with my worldview and sense of self. I lost my idol that day—my god.

But, you know what? I gained myself. It opened a doorway for me to trust in my ability to endure, my wherewithal, and my innate strength. It ultimately established a richer spiritual understanding than I ever had prior. It was precisely what needed to happen—even though I didn't want it.

Had I stayed part of that tradition, I would never have been permitted to spread my energetic wings. I would never have been allowed to develop aspects of my meditative abilities that were considered taboo. I was suddenly allowed to practice with other teachers, use other mantras, study in other traditions—things that were always forbidden because we were instructed to never search for wisdom beyond the guru. I began to relish my personal power rather than give it away. I began to find what nourished me through my own explorations—not what someone else said I needed.

Experiencing this immensely painful karma actually turned me into an integrated, realized person. I grew tremendously through the experience.

But, fuck, it was hard. My sense of faith, my sense of trust, and my sense of certainty were rubbed away. I thought I had known the direction my life was headed—I thought I knew the contours of the bedrock on which I was building my life—but everything was demolished. I had to rebuild my world, my plans, and my spiritual sense of selfhood. It was excruciating—but it was precisely what I needed for my next level of personal growth.

In hindsight, I have gotten to the point where I am profoundly glad they threw me out. I would never have left of my own volition—I would have stayed in perpetuity (largely because there was no graceful way to go—once you were in, you stayed in). Had my world not been demolished for me, I would have continued on in that self-limited state, never knowing my full potential.

I learned that I could survive the unimaginable. To put it into perspective, imagine how it would feel to a Christian if Jesus showed up on Earth to resurrect all souls, but turned to them and said, "Meh. Not you, though. Sorry, kid." That's how it felt. My savior had abandoned me. I was isolated, alone, and damned.

At least, that's how it seemed in the beginning. Over time, I began to see things anew. I came to view my former teacher as fallible—human. I adjusted my internal compass, set new demarcations on the horizon, and sought new vantages—ones that were better aligned and healthier for me. That process of discernment was heart-wrenching—it is not something I would wish on anyone. I have heard stories of others considering suicide when faced with a similar excommunication from their spiritual tradition. But the struggle toward my new path made me robustly strong. It made me into the man I am. I am immensely grateful for my guru breaking my heart.

That leads me to the last thing I want to say about the people who hurt you—who destroy your worldview and sense of self: hallelujah. Thank heavens for them. Bless them.

Because they just did you a huge service.

> *"Life doesn't give you the people you want, it gives you the people you need: to love you, to hate you, to make you, to break you, and to make you the person you were meant to be."*
> — **Walt Whitman, poet and journalist**

MEDITATION XII

Close your eyes and take a deep breath. Try to sink your mind's eye into the center of your core. Feel the life you hoped to live—the crystalline castles you built in your mind. Center on the hopes you've created for "someday" and "somewhere" and "somewhen."

Imagine your perfect life as being a sparkling, opalescent bubble. Perfect and round. And, with a deep inhale, invite the bubble to pop.

It isn't real. None of it.

Your imaginings. Your illusions. Your hopes and dreams.

All that we have that is real is what is around us. We cannot be anything other than what we really are. We cannot live a life that is different than our own.

Sink into the wetness that is your core. Wallow in the sadness that is the disappointment of the loss of your alternative life.

You are not going to be the person you hoped—you are not going to live the life of which you've dreamt.

But, better than that, you *are* going to get to be you. Unique. Irreplaceable. Authentic. Totally different from anyone else.

If you had an image of what your life was going to look like—then it was based on other people's journeys. You have no knowledge of the turns and crossings your life is going to take. If you can envision it, then it is a story you encountered somewhere—it's based on a book your read or a film you watched. Your life will be different from everyone else's—it is impossible to know it full-out. Open yourself up to possibility. Open yourself up to opportunity.

You are going to have a life that is so much grander than anything you could have ever dreamt up. But, in order to get it, you have to be willing to face the wild unknown. Step into the darkness. Surrender to curiosity. You have no control here. Trust that a higher awareness is arranging the lessons you need to learn, the people you need to meet, the hardships you have to face.

Realize that, whatever comes, it will teach you valuable lessons for your growth. It will be a wild ride—sometimes arching high in the sky, sometimes sinking low in a valley. Some say that we choose our lessons before we are born. Some say our past actions dictate our karma. Regardless, sink into the knowledge that life will continue, you are a passenger on the ride, and all you can do is be open in wonder to whatever comes next. Shout a hearty "yes" to your adventure. Be willing to embrace whatever is ahead.

You are perfect—just as you are. Life is manifesting just as it needs to. You don't need to "do" anything—simply be. Enjoy what life brings. We are all ultimately powerless.

Come back to your body when you are ready.

"You were born with wings, why prefer to crawl through life?"
— **Rumi, Sufi poet and philosopher**

I remember traveling in Mexico with my mother once, and she brought us to a shaman. We huddled together with other (mostly white) spiritual aspirants in clothing that ranged from swimming suits to loincloths—in a smoke-filled yurt. A fire burned in the middle, making the space unbearably hot. A few people lay passed out from the temperature against the walls. In the middle stood a diminutive man with skin like a crumpled paper bag. He wielded eagle feathers, rattles, and bowls of heaven-knows-what.

I didn't understand much of what he was singing or saying—seeing as I don't speak a lick of Spanish. But I don't think Spanish was the language in which he was chanting. There were a few moments when he would flip into English and instruct us to do things. And there was one particular instance that I remember vividly, even from my sweaty, almost-at-heatstroke stupor. He asked us to call to mind the people that have hurt us, our worst enemies, the one's we've never forgiven—and *bless* them. His instructions went something like this.

Think of the people in your life who have caused you the greatest harm. Imagine those individuals who broke your heart, tried to destroy you, stole something you valued dearly. As you bring them to mind, I want you to bless them.

We often offer blessings for our friends—blessings for our family. We even bless people we don't even know, strangers. But we should always start by blessing the people for whom you still hold anger. Still hold hate. One, because it'll dissolve the negative bond between the two of you. Two, wishing them to heal, to be blessed, to be in a better state, might keep them from damaging other people. After all, most strike out due to their own pain. Help these individuals heal their wounds, and it might save others from their wrath. Third, by blessing them—sending them positive feelings—will open the door to that important emotion in yourself: forgiveness. Realize that they taught you a valuable lesson that you needed to learn, and thank them for it. Even if it was immensely painful at the time—realize how much more you know now from that experience. See how you've grown.

It was the first time I'd ever done that. I thought about the people in the ashram. I thought of how crushed I was when they sent me off like that—after my years of service. And, for the first time since that initial heartbreak, I did what he suggested. I *blessed* them.

It's so important that we send good vibes to the people who have taught us our deepest lessons—even if they were immensely painful ones. Bless our exes, our evil fourth-grade teachers, our misguided parents. We need to forgive and release our negative feelings. I found the shaman's words a beautiful description of how I could heal and move on in the wake of my spiritual tradition's abrupt departure. It gave me a language and perspective for my own healing.

I would like for us to explore this practice together—inviting release and wellbeing for all the people in our sphere. Even the evil ones.

EXERCISE

Go ahead and find a beautiful place to sit—by water, on a mountaintop, or in a mediation space that you've cultivated. Envision yourself surrounded by white light—or, if you are someone who believes in angels or higher beings, you can imagine them circling you, consecrating a sacred area for healing.

Take a few moments to breathe and center yourself. When you are ready, imagine someone who has disappointed you, hurt you, or who you resent—imagine them stepping into the circle and standing across from you.

Notice what emotions arise within. Keep breathing, and witness your intense feelings. Don't try to change them, just let them be as they are.

Quietly, when you're ready, place your hands over the center of your chest and cultivate a sense of gratitude or love. Imagine a sphere of light beneath your fingertips—and, once it's steady, offer your hands and the light out toward the person across from you. Bless them. Offer them your highest sense of health, energy, and healing. Let that light flow off of you and into them.

As you do, quietly say: "I bless you—wish you your highest happiness—and I am letting you go."

Bring your hands back to your heart and repeat this practice again.

Your goal is to fill yourself and the person across from you with as much love, as much light, and with as many blessings as is possible. The Buddha said, "Holding onto anger is like grasping a hot coal with the intent of throwing it at someone else; you are the one who gets burned." We have to release our feelings of hate, animosity, or disappointment. We have to fill the people of our focus and ourselves with unconditional love—even those who have enacted horrible atrocities against us. Offer them healing—even if it's just so that they become well and not hurt others again. Bless them to the best of your abilities.

Once they/you are as full as you can manage, invite them to de-

261

part. Imagine any cords of energy connecting the two of you dissolving as they go. You don't need to think of them or give them any more energy. Love them and release them.

You can say, "I love you, and I'm letting you go."

You may stop here or continue on with another person/entity.

Whenever you are done, imagine water flowing through you, draining away any toxicity that came up. Feel it flow into the earth, cleansing you, carrying away any debris. Find peace with where you are. Feel whole. You are enough.

> "A sense of calm came over me. More and more often, I found myself thinking, 'This is where I belong. This is what I came into this world to do.'"
> — **Jane Goodall, primatologist and anthropologist**

As we give up controlling our destiny—as we embrace the bittersweet tang of our own inability to formulate the life we desire—it is normal to experience regret. And with that regret, we must come to terms with the notion of forgiveness—both for ourselves and others. Until you can forgive your life for not meeting your expectations, for not being good enough—you will never be fully ready to move on. Until you can forgive others for their slights, you will never permit yourself to fully heal.

The most important—and most challenging—person we ultimately need to forgive is ourselves. We have disappointed ourselves so many times, over and again. We have made ourselves promises and broken them. We have told ourselves that we would be a certain type of person, manifest a certain destiny, exist a certain way. This latest blow, realizing that you will never have the life you always envisioned, is possibly one of the toughest disappointments you'll face. You are never going to become the person you thought you would when you were younger. That life is over. You have let your childhood "you" down.

It's important to let this settle in—to truly accept it. Your younger self is not going to get what they wanted. Further, you must remain gracious and patient with yourself. As you come closer to your innate truth, you will see more clearly that those desired demarcations of success were just temporary place holders for real self-worth. Your younger self did not have the understanding or capacity to recognize what you genuinely needed for fulfillment. In fact, the trappings of the life you hoped to live might not have made you lastingly happy at all. Your external desires werelike trophies—they would have brought fleeting euphoria before being shoved onto a mantle and forgotten. Trophies don't continually spark joy.

From my point of view, the only goals that truly matter are learning to be happy and fully satisfied. I ask myself if I can be gracious, at ease, and at home with myself regardless of external circumstances. No matter what is going on superficially—can I be peaceful, relaxed, and contented on a deeper level? Can I find comfort within my body and mind, despite winning or losing? Can I dwell in joy, regardless of experiencing momentary happiness or grief? Can I be grateful for being me, whether I am lauded as a success or condemned as a failure?

This pursuit is a tall order—and is diametrically opposite of what the modern world tells us we need in order to be happy. Intrinsic joy does not dwell with hordes of wealth, luxury items, a bevy of models in bikinis, nor a seaside mansion. It is not having everything you want. It is about being happy with where you are. Being here, now. Peace of mind is a much greater characteristic of lasting happiness. If I can find a peaceful state that lasts despite external changes—then I have so much of what I need.

> *"In the end, only three things matter: how much you loved, how gently you lived, and how gracefully you let go of things not meant for you."*
> — **Jack Kornfield, writer and teacher**

The more we witness the transient nature of life, the more we realize how quickly external circumstances change. Piles of riches can collapse into debt faster than the stock market meeting a worldwide pandemic. The fragile beauty of youth can sag into weathered old age faster than the turn of a calendar page. Good health can evaporate with one slip of a heavy barbell at the gym. It is the only constant we can count on—change. If we can accept that life will always be moving in new directions—if we can be happy regardless of wherever it heads—then we have won. We have attained a level of flourishing that few achieve—and no one can take it from us.

The good news is that anyone can do it. I started off this journey as one of the most insecure, disconnected, paralytically afraid, closeted, and self-deluding individuals I've ever known. If I found the wherewithal to traverse the rocky terrain of personal dissatisfaction—then you can, too. I genuinely love my life—but it took me a hell of a lot of work to get here. And that's is not to say that I still don't have rough days—I definitely do. There are plenty of mornings where insufficiency rears its head, and I feel insignificant. But, fortunately, those days become rarer and rarer. For the most part, I feel exceedingly blessed. I wouldn't trade my life for anyone else's—and there were many years where I would never have been able to honestly say that.

We have come so far together—and I am honored to be walking with you. It's critical that we hold onto the notion that profound satisfaction can happen anywhere—you need no special awards, job, or partner to attain it. You can be radically happy wherever you find yourself. It is a tremendous boon to see that where you are, right now, is enough. You are perfect—you are whole—you are precisely where you should be. And no matter what happens next, you can trust that you're going to thrive. Believe in yourself.

> *"I do not exist to impress the world. I exist to live my life in a way that will make me happy."*
> — **Richard Bach, writer and spiritualist**

Close your eyes, and for this meditation, lean back onto a pillow or the floor.

Feel your body going limp. Feel your feet relax, your calves, your thighs—all of your legs. Feel your belly soften, your heart open, your shoulders drop. Feel your arms becoming heavy. Your neck releases, your head rocks gently side to side.

I want you to envision sunlight filtering through tree branches overhead—it's a beautiful, crisp day. Your body is effortlessly light, and you are lying on the back of an enormous leaf—traveling down a wide river. The trees flit overhead, and the light flickers across your face, casting dancing shadows. You feel the motion of the gentle current under you, pulling you along. You have no concern about steering your vessel—you know that the water will guide you safely around debris, over rocks, and beyond whirlpools. The water is carrying you on the most efficient course to reach your destination.

You can relax and feel nature supporting you, leading you. All is exactly as it is supposed to be. You have no desire to fight, to change, to be in control. Instead, you have fully given over to the flow of life—things are exactly as they should be. Mother Nature has the power—and just as she guides the changing of the seasons or the flow from day to night, she is carrying you safely and efficiently. There's nothing that needs doing—nothing to be done. You can let go of fear—simply let yourself be. A higher power has you and is not going to let go.

Let life carry you along to your perfect destination. Feel the ripples of current under the leaf, under your raft. Travel cradled in the embrace of life. You are exactly where you need to be—let all else fall away. You are enough. This moment is enough. Give up everything.

> *"Do not judge me by my successes; judge me by how many times I fell down and got back up again."*
> — **Nelson Mandela, civil rights activist and political leader**

In contemporary America, we are obsessed with manifesting our destiny. We fervently believe that if we can imagine an outcome, then it is within our right to make it a reality. Or, as Walt Disney blithely said, "If you can dream it, you can do it." With all respect to Mister Disney (and my mother, who bought me my first copy of Rhonda Bryne's *The Secret* when I was only thirteen years old), this is a load of bull-crap.

No—you cannot manifest the life of your dreams with surgical precision. No, you cannot decide that you are going to simply be a certain way and—poof—it magically happens. In fact, you can be a wonderfully positive-thinking person who visualizes and meditates on success and still fails miserably by all external standards. And that's totally okay—failure is an immense learning tool. Losing out is a great teacher.

You may eat the right food, perform the correct forms of exercise—and still be out of shape. You might invest wisely, work hard—and still be pinching pennies. You might put in the hours of hard work, meet the right people—and still fail to see your career taking off. And this is okay.

We Americans love the notion that we live in a meritocratic society where a person's effort directly correlates with their level of success—and reflect their worth as a human being. If you become a billionaire by writing computer software—you are told that you are a genius. If you serve burgers at a fast-food restaurant and are nearing thirty—you are a doofus. Success in the world mirrors a person's value—but we self-examining people know this to not be true. We've seen time and again that the happiest, most well-adjusted people are many times not the ones at the top of the pyramid. Often, the enlightened saints are the ones serving in the streets, covered in filth, and living in ways that others would not deign to emulate. Similarly, as previously discussed, the men and women in the echelons of outward success can be immensely unhappy, unfulfilled, and unscrupulous in their behaviors.

Instead of viewing our lives as being meaningful based on what we achieved—we should shift our focus to our intent. What did we strive for? What were the efforts we put in—rather than the results we attained? Striving for growth should hold merit—not the outcomes, which are largely the result of luck and destiny. Becoming rich and famous is outside of our control—and anyone who has attained these heights will tell you how it was pure happenstance that propelled them and not the next, equally talented and hard-working individual beside them.

> *"Maybe you'll marry, maybe you won't. Maybe you'll have children, maybe you won't. Maybe you'll divorce at 40, maybe you'll dance the funky chicken on your 75th wedding anniversary. Whatever you do, don't congratulate yourself too much, or berate yourself either. Your choices are half chance. So are everybody else's."*
> — **Mary Schmich, journalist and writer**

We Americans live in a fantasyland where we assert that anyone can become anything their heart desires—but this is simply not reality. Very few can warp the physical world—like a telekinetic bending spoons with their mind—and those that are able aren't necessarily the happiest. Just because someone is able to use their will to force something into existence doesn't mean that they will ultimately be more satisfied. Worldly success does not equate to joy—and the ability to manifest it does not make someone a more worthwhile human being.

Control is an illusion, and the sooner you can surrender willfulness, the sooner lasting satisfaction will arise. Find joy in letting go and letting life take control. This notion that if we only tried harder, wanted it more, or strove harder is making us sick and miserable. We should shift those same efforts to being grateful for what we've been given and making the best out of our current situations. What if, instead of rejecting the blessings that are before us, we appreciated the opportunities each of us has in our lives? What if we relished the situations we find ourselves in and use them for growth? What if we each notice our privilege or immense wealth (regardless of income) and feel gratitude for what we have? We would all be so much happier. You already have everything that you need, if you look closely. Life has given you the tools and abilities to learn from your present circumstances.

The reality that all of us have to face sooner or later is karma. We already discussed this topic in a previous chapter, I know. But, to take our previous conversations one step further: karma is the lessons that you need to learn, the actions that you have to take, and the experiences that you need to live through. You came into this life with baggage—and you are going to have to pay the carry-on fee. No amount of magical thinking will allow you to fart fairy dust and ride a unicorn to a land where you are unaccountable to your past actions—where you can live devoid of repercussions. Every action will have an opposite and equal reaction—it is Newton's third law of physics. There is no escaping karma.

This is in no way a bad thing. The life that you've attracted is what you need to go through in order to come into wholeness. Based on what you've previously done, said, or enacted—life is giving you the opportunity to learn from those choices and understand that you are more than the amalgamation of your wants and desires. You are a spirit having a human experience, and the goal of this life is to evolve to the next level. Why would you want to escape the lessons you need to learn? Wouldn't it be better to take those lessons, use them, and level-up as a soul? If you can accept what karma is bringing into your life—you will awaken. You will become freer, be able to better find joy—whether someone else sees you as "rich" or "poor," "blessed" or "damned," "fortunate" or "unfortunate."

Nothing is either good or bad—only thinking makes it so. Get past the duality of trying to manifest a "good" life, and enjoy the life you have. Each of us has so many blessings, if only we choose to see them. We need to give up the illusion of being able to control our destiny and leap into the waters of what's here now. If the rain comes down, let it pool—and then climb aboard the canoe that life provides and chart the seas ahead. We don't need to be anywhere else but where we are—we don't need to live any life but our own. Be here, now. Everything you need already exists.

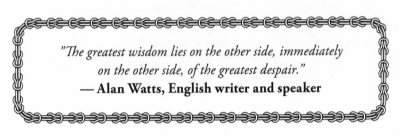

> *"The greatest wisdom lies on the other side, immediately on the other side, of the greatest despair."*
> — **Alan Watts, English writer and speaker**

SUMMARY:

— **You are probably not going to have the life you imagined. As you've grown, what you want and need has changed. Em brace it.**

— **Forgive everyone—most of all, yourself. We are all doing the best we can, and sometimes we disappoint ourselves.**

— **Learn to accept what is. Karma is a great teacher—and the life you have is giving you the lessons you need to learn.**

Chapter 10:

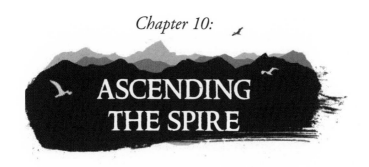

ASCENDING THE SPIRE

*"The best way to find yourself, is to lose yourself
in the service of others."*
— **Mahatma Gandhi, activist and spiritual leader**

W e have spent the previous nine chapters of this book examining you from every angle. Who are you when you're alone? What are the things that scare you? How might your identity be different than you supposed? How are you connected with your body, your social circles, your word choices, and the stories you share? How do they change as you come to know yourself better? We have attacked the notion of identity and wholeness from a very self-centric perspective. But one's life cannot be lived entirely focused on one's self. In order to find true release into our inner state of belonging, we have to wrangle with forces beyond our conceptions of ourselves.

One of the best ways to truly find contentment inside is to live for something greater than one's own wants and needs. A life lived for servicing one's own pleasure is often shallow. By comparison, a life dedicated to the betterment of some cause or mission often leads to depth and generosity. When we live in this way, we become benevolent of spirit. We feel gracious, relaxed, and grateful for all that we have been awarded.

It really doesn't matter so much what that cause is. It could be a family member that you help take care of, a romantic partner you support with love, or the raising of a child. It could be a volunteer project, an entrepreneurial organization, or a community group. The point is, when we start dedicating our energy, time, and focus to something beyond ourselves—we start to put the collective good at the forefront. We appreciate the interconnectedness of all life and how, by serving another, we are actually enhancing our own wellbeing.

It's hard to feel bad for yourself when you're helping someone else. This is why so many spiritual traditions throughout time have recommended enacting selfless service. Some may call it a mission trip, others *seva*—regardless, the idea is the same. By helping others, we become more generous, enthusiastic, and less self-absorbed.

Of course, we need time for reflection and self-inquiry, but a lifetime dedicated to only one's own wellbeing is a life devoid of the pleasure of fellowship, kinship, and a sense of belonging. We have all experienced the joy of completing a group project or presenting someone else with an object of their desire. The shared exuberance makes us feel fulfilled. There is immense joy in feeling like we are living aligned with our mission, our life's calling.

We are social animals—we have evolved to exist as members of a tribe. As we discussed in an earlier chapter, loneliness is hardwired into our DNA to be detrimental to our health and wellbeing. We thrive when we connect with others and put someone else's good ahead of our own. It doesn't even need to be a human—focusing on improving the wellbeing of an animal or the environment can be equally fulfilling.

A recent study by the University of Washington's Institute for Learning and Brain Sciences shows that even babies demonstrate altruistic tendencies. Without prompting, fifty-eight percent of the infants studied would offer their own food to a researcher who dropped theirs and seemed unable to reach it.[1] Even with infants who had been denied their mid-day snack, a whopping thirty-seven percent of the hungry little ones opted to give the researcher their blueberry rather than eat it themselves.

I personally derive tremendous satisfaction from dedicating myself to the rehabilitation of our prickly rescue-dog. His mother lived on the streets of the South and was scheduled to be euthanized—even while pregnant with her litter of pups. A Chicago-based animal group rescued her—and my partner and I welcomed one of her little ones into our home. By that point, though, our dog had already been exposed to a significant amount of trauma. He had been shipped from one foster guardian to another, separated from his mom and siblings, crated for far too many hours, and had developed aggressive tendencies. To be blunt, he was a jerk when we took him in.

Over time and with tremendous patience, he has grown into a kind adult dog. He is emotionally intelligent, considerate, and environmentally aware. I feel immense pride in witnessing his evolution—knowing that we've given him a better life than he might have had without us. My husband and I frequently discuss how other people maybe wouldn't have had the patience to redirect him from his aggressive tendencies—they likely would have surrendered him to a shelter, where he would have been put down. It has been a labor of love to heal him, but it is one that I have found immensely rewarding. He is a wonderful companion—and it's all so much more meaningful for me to know that I have helped him thrive.

For those of you who have never been animal owners, the devotion we demonstrate might seem perplexing—but it boils down to giving and receiving love. I'm not just living for myself—I am living for the wellbeing of another.

As Mother Teresa said, "There are no great things, only small things with great love." A grandmother cooking and cleaning up after her grandchildren—that is an act of love. Having supper waiting for your romantic partner when you know they've had a rough day—that's one, too. Often, we assume that it is the grandiose gestures that prove our devotion—but, in fact, it's often the opposite. It's showing up day after day, even when you don't want to, even when you're tired. Those little moments demonstrate that you care. It's taking the time to listen and remember the important facts and figures of another person's life. It's about showing up when you say you will.

We demonstrate our generosity by the regularity with which we enact benevolence. Instead of one, huge gesture—make countless smaller ones. Tiny acts of kindness can erect massive towers over time—built up stone by stone. Think of this in your own relationships—what has better built trust and devotion between you and your significant others? The dozens of flowers they shipped to you one Valentine's Day—or the fact that they're willing to massage your shoulders and listen to you when you come home from work each night? Was it the one-time extravagance that they arranged—or was it the smaller, subtle reassurances that they care, that you matter to them? Tiny gestures can have resounding echoes.

> "The mystery of human existence lies not in just staying alive,
> but in finding something to live for."
> — **Fyodor Dostoyevsky, Russian writer**

I'd be remiss to not address the other creature living in our home—my husband. Being in communion with a partner has taught me some of my greatest lessons—and consciously working on our relationship has instructed me on how to live for something greater than myself. The wellbeing of our partnership is at the forefront of my mind. What can I do to keep us nourished, satiated, and growing in the same direction? How can I make the best life possible for the two of us?

I would like to share a little story about when we met. I was twenty-seven—and at that point, I had more or less given up on dating. I had been out for a few years and had experienced a dearth of quality guys. Even the ones I invited back for third and fourth dates ended up proving lackluster or incompatible. I wanted a connection that gave me so much more than just a warm body to come home to. I desired someone who would kindle my imagination and light a fire of exploration inside my soul. I wanted to be with someone who would inspire me to be my best self, lead by example, and possess a profound understanding of exploring the fullness of existence. I wanted a spirit companion to wander the frontiers of becoming whole with me.

I had entered relationships with a handful of men, but even they ended up being not what I sensed I needed. A few broke my heart—but I was, ultimately, glad to see them go. Not finding what I needed, I figured that I would just focus on living my life and let someone come into it if they were meant to find me. I left my dating profile active online but only replied to men who messaged me—I wasn't planning on actively seeking anyone out. I didn't want to lock every door or board up every window into my life—I wanted to stay open to possibilities—I just didn't want to keep forcing something that wasn't happening. Well, you know how the old saying goes—once you stop looking, what you're searching for comes for you.

My husband was just relocating from California to Chicago for work, with a friend helping him move. After three days of unboxing and assembling furniture, his friend headed home. Before he departed, however, he mentioned that he had been meeting quality guys on this one, particular dating site—and he encouraged my now-husband to check it out.

Newly alone in the city, he started work the following day. That weekend, he decided to set up a profile on that site. My profile was one of the very first he came across—and he felt a spark of recognition. He sensed that I was the person for whom he was searching—the man that he hoped was out there. He sent me a private message and crossed his fingers.

I happened to be boarding a plane to Mexico when I got his message request. Scanning his pictures, I felt my stomach lurch. Though I didn't know that my soon-to-be-partner was experiencing the same, I too felt this sense of knowing, this sense of cosmic alignment. I wrote him back.

Though I was traveling abroad for six days, we became fast friends. Our in-app messages swiftly developed into texts, which became phone calls, and then video chats. By the third day of texting, we had already said, "I love you"—despite my fears about progressing too fast. And by the end of the week, I heard a voice during my morning meditation that said, "You may have met your future husband." At the airport, I bought a postcard to write him a note telling him that I was his life partner. Not too overly enthusiastic or bold, was I?

I took a taxi directly from the airport to our first date and handed him the postcard. He was even more thrilling in person than I was anticipating—and we've been by each other's side ever since. He was the partner I would have designed, if I could—we complement and contrast each other so well. He is my soul's match, my "twin flame"—and I am grateful each and every single day to get to love and cherish him.

He has helped me know myself better than I could have anticipated. By adventuring together, our relationship has revealed to one another a deeper experience of our personal truths. As the author Tina Welling has written, "Partners meant two people who shared the experience of becoming their full selves." This has definitely been our experience. We have blossomed in the pursuit of a shared life.

Now, I do openly acknowledge that our type of connection is unusual—not everyone has such strong soul-contracts to meet in this lifetime. My husband and I strongly believe that we chose to incarnate together before being born to accomplish a specific mission. We were what each other needed in order to grow into our full potential—and being with each other allows us to make the world a better place via our collective contributions. I recognize if this sounds a little surreal, but this is honestly how we feel.

While I do think that our type of relationship is unique—I also believe that any meaningful partnership can teach you about your essence. You can learn from anyone who knows you well—they can be your guide, your teacher, and help point the way toward your ecstatic self. You get reflected and refracted in the eyes of your beloved—your curves shine across their angles and edges. We can know ourselves better by seeing how we interact with another, the kind of person we attract, and the way the relationship matures. You can see outer manifestations of where you are internally through aspects of your partnership.

My husband's happiness and satisfaction mean a tremendous amount to me—being his partner gives my life context and meaning. I have a richer, fuller life by serving our collective wellbeing. So, too, do I find satisfaction in being my dog's keeper. It is these soul connections that have helped me grow, deepen my root system within myself, and become a more beneficent spirit. Serving them has given me more to live for.

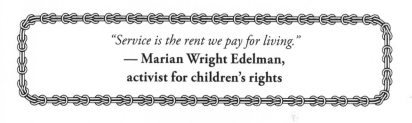

"Service is the rent we pay for living."
— **Marian Wright Edelman,**
activist for children's rights

EXERCISE

Nearly everyone on this planet wants to find their perfect soulmate. Whether this may or may not happen depends upon karma (the lessons you need to learn to bring you into balance). Regardless of our fate, we all can actively choose to couple with partners who tremendously benefit us. Through some quick analysis, we can estimate the potential of a prospective friend/romantic interest/business partner. We can discern how well a possible journey-mate might be to complement our paths.

Too many of us choose relationships (platonic or otherwise) for superficial reasons—the other person looks good, has money, or—simply—happens to just be the person that's available presently. But, ultimately, these may not be the optimal reasons to draw people into our lives. Instead, we should clarify the qualities we actually need and/ or want—and make decisions regarding our personal connections from there.

A mentor of mine once gave me a three-column list for assessing potential partners of any kind, and I would like to share this categorization system with you. It's a simple yet profound way to go about evaluating the potential of any new person who enters your sphere—and what they might be able to offer you energetically. If you are currently swimming in the dating pool, this can also be a nice way to cull the list of your potential suitors. You can weed out a vast swath of possible paramours before you make first overtures.

The first question you should ask yourself is: what qualities do I absolutely "need" in a person with whom I am going to be engaged in a relationship? Qualities might include integrity, honesty, self-awareness, optimism, or a sense of humor. The items on this list will change from time to time as you come to know yourself better. You may discover that something you initially identified as a "need" might actually be more of a "want"—and vice versa. Be careful of naming anything too outwardly specific as a need. Beautiful people can arrive in untraditional packaging. It would be a shame to turn away your soulmate just because they're a brunette—and you normally only ever consider gingers.

Qualities I require in someone with whom I am in relationship:

The next list is the things you "want" to have in a person—but they aren't necessarily deal-breakers. As long as someone has more than a few of these items, you can give them consideration. Like the list prior, it is entirely possible that you might start off with some items on this list and realize that they actually ought to be shifted to "needs." Perhaps you assumed that being able to make light of a difficult situation was only a "want"—but, over time, you discover that it's actually a fundamental quality that you require for someone with whom you share intimacy. Feel free to continue exploring what you truly want, and then adjust accordingly.

Qualities I would enjoy in a partner:

_____   _____   _____
_____   _____   _____
_____   _____   _____
_____   _____   _____
_____   _____   _____
_____   _____   _____
_____   _____   _____
_____   _____   _____
_____   _____   _____
_____   _____   _____
_____   _____   _____
_____   _____   _____

The last list, no surprise, pertains to personal boundaries. What are the qualities that you absolutely refuse to tolerate in a potential significant other or collaborator? Where are your lines-in-the-sand that should not be crossed? Again, stay flexible—you may be surprised what items do or do not belong in this "deal breakers" list.

Aspects that I will not tolerate in a partner:

———————————   ———————————   ———————————
———————————   ———————————   ———————————
———————————   ———————————   ———————————
———————————   ———————————   ———————————
———————————   ———————————   ———————————
———————————   ———————————   ———————————
———————————   ———————————   ———————————
———————————   ———————————   ———————————
———————————   ———————————   ———————————
———————————   ———————————   ———————————
———————————   ———————————   ———————————
———————————   ———————————   ———————————

From here, it's important to stay open and see who steps into your life. This can also be a useful tool for evaluating your current relationships—family, friends, etc. You may be surprised about behaviors you've put up with that are inimical to your best interests.

> "People are like stained-glass windows. They sparkle and shine when the sun is out, but when the darkness sets in, their true beauty is revealed only if there is a light from within."
> — **Elisabeth Kübler-Ross, writer and death researcher**

One of the things that come to mind for me with the previous exercise is the notion of boundaries. As you come to know yourself and your worth better, you are going to become less tolerant of people treating you poorly. You may already find that, through our explorations, you are establishing more defined boundaries behind which people are expected to remain.

Many of us permit unwelcome behaviors or tolerate inappropriate actions because we believe that is all we deserve. As we continue to discover that we are worthy of love, kindness, compassion, and integrity—we demand the same from others. You start to say, "No—I will not be treated that way." You stop making excuses for people's poor decisions and inconsiderate actions. You know that you are worth being treated with respect and dignity—you know that your life has value and that others should treat you accordingly. This is not egotism—this is a simple truth that applies to every sentient being on the planet. We all deserve respect.

As I said in an earlier chapter, don't be surprised if certain relationships in your life change as you continue to evolve. The melodic harmonies inside of you are maturing, your notes are blending in different frequencies than before. As your internal symphony morphs, the people who feel like they are in consort with you are going to shift. Old friends, old hangouts, and old patterns may seem less enticing. As we understand and respect ourselves more, we demand better—not in a selfish way, but in a way of showing respect for the blessings we have been given.

Because, whether we actively acknowledge it or not, each of us has been truly gifted. We are all brilliant—each of us possesses genius. We have beautiful blessings that we have historically been taught to devalue. The Buddhists call it having a "precious human life"—we have the gifts of the opportunity to grow, connect inside, and become our best selves. Every one of us has been awarded opportunities, talents, skills, and passions. We are all living in abundance—if only we will consciously recognize it.

What are your gifts? I know you have them. Studying them might provide you with insights on the ways in which you're able to give back to the world. What do you have to offer that might be of benefit to people like you? How can you "pay it forward" and use what you've learned/cultivated/realized to aid others in their journeys onward?

> "There is almost a sensual longing for communion with others who have a large vision. The immense fulfillment of the friendship between those engaged in furthering the evolution of consciousness has a quality impossible to describe."
> — **Pierre Teilhard de Chardin, French philosopher and Jesuit priest**

MEDITATION XIV

Close your eyes and take a deep breath.

You are perfect. You are beautiful. You are talented, gifted, and living a life of abundance.

How do these words make you feel? Do you shrink back at all? Have any thoughts arisen like, "Who am I to be amazing? Who am I to think of myself as rich?"

We have been trained by a world that emphasizes our insufficiencies. Each day, we see advertisements that shout, "You are not pretty enough—but if you buy our face cream, your partner won't be able to keep his hands off you." They scream, "You won't be happy unless you purchase our Greek yogurt."

Can you recognize the absurdity in this? You are *already* radiant. You are already whole. Even if you don't have as much as you would like, you already have so much more than you need to survive.

Do you realize that you are living in one of the most abundant periods in human history? Fewer people live in poverty than ever before. More people have access to clean running water, shelter, interior heat and cooling, entertainment, produce, and clothing than at any point in the last many centuries? You are so blessed. We are all so blessed.

Countless diseases have been eradicated. The temperature is habitable for most of the year—we aren't in an ice age where glaciers cover most of the planet. You are living in a golden time of abundance and grace.

Start to think of all the things in your life for which you could be grateful. Name them, visualize them, and offer thanks in an upwards direction. We could all sit here for hours and still come up with new gifts to name—the list of what we have to be thankful for is inexhaustible.

I encourage you to sit here for many minutes, dwelling in gratitude and thanking your lucky stars for all the benefits you have in your life. You are so immensely blessed. You need nothing to complete you—you are already perfect—you just need to see it.

> *"To leave the world a bit better, whether by a healthy child, a garden patch, or a redeemed social condition; to know even one life breathed easier because you loved.*
> *This is to have succeeded."*
> — **Ralph Waldo Emerson, essayist and philosopher**

EXERCISE

What are the ways in which you feel called to benefit the world? What are your interests, your skills, and your hobbies? Again, it doesn't need to be a massive undertaking. It could be volunteering to teach kids to play chess in a city park. It could be going once a month to help your mom clear out her attic. What more can you live for? Dream up some ideas of things/persons/causes that you could donate your time/expertise/energy.

Things I enjoy doing and would provide benefit for another living being:

_____

_____

_____

_____

_____

_____

_____

_____

_____

_____

_____

_____

_____

_____

How can you practically implement these ideas? Get specific here. What are some identified times/places/ways you could engage with these plans? What are the next steps to make these aspirations a reality? Hold yourself accountable for following through. Positive intentions are great—but actions are even better. Follow through.

I can implement these ideas by:

_____

_____

_____

_____

_____

_____

_____

_____

_____

_____

_____

_____

_____

Good work. Stepping outside of yourself can be intimidating. Though we know it'll feel good when we're done, volunteering our time can feel like a tall hurdle—it requires a leap of faith. Get it done—and once you have completed your act(s) of service, journal about your experience below.

Journal on how it feels to be of service:

_____

_____

_____

_____

_____

_____

_____

_____

_____

_____

_____

_____

_____

_____

_____

_____

_____

_____

_____

> "A human being is a part of the whole, called by us Universe, a part limited in time and space. He experiences himself, his thoughts and feelings as something separated from the rest—a kind of optical delusion of his consciousness. This delusion is a kind of prison, restricting us to our personal desires and to affection for a few persons nearest to us. Our task must be to free ourselves from this prison by widening our circle of compassion to embrace all living creatures and all of nature in its beauty. The true value of a human being is determined primarily by the measure and the sense in which he has attained liberation from the self."
> — **Albert Einstein, atomic physicist and watchmaker**

Your life is precious. *You* are precious. As we discuss the idea of living for something greater, we would be remiss if we did not apply that notion to our sense of self, too. In this section, we are going to explore the idea of soulfulness. Who are you at your deepest essence? Cultures throughout time have called that deepest part of ourselves numerous things—soul, *atman, ka,* Holy Spirit, *sanhunqipo*—but these words all refer to the same, cosmic spark.

We are moving from the firm lands of logic that we have (mostly) dealt with for the previous parts of the book and galloping into the realms of myth and fog. Places where ideas are as fragile and as tender as gossamer strands—and I am going to ask you to set your speculating self aside. I am going to ask you to abandon logic and quantifiable measuring—they are not going to serve you here. Instead, I entice you to adopt a sense of wonder, curiosity, and an openness. You are going to need to listen for truth from the space between your heartbeats—centered in an organ that doesn't understand words. There is a knowing that comes without thought, an understanding that happens without mind.

Step with me into the dark pool of awareness inside your core.

And from that space, recognize this ineffable truth: the you that you are seeking does not exist—at least, in the limited sense. There is no "you" as we conventionally describe it. Instead, there is only a "You"—with a capital Y. There is a cosmic, stardust-derived, spirit essence that is intrinsically connected to every organic and inorganic element in creation. You are an unknowable creature because the reality of You is something beyond time, space, or recognition.

I know that this can be a disorienting and disconcerting idea to accept. So, in order to illustrate what I am describing, I am going to do what spiritual teachers throughout history have done. I am going to share with you a story:

> One day, long ago, a man searched high and low for knowledge of his true self. In despair, lacking answers, he turned his query to a great guru. This spiritual teacher was renowned for comprehending the great mysteries of life. She understood the orbits of the planets, the journeys souls undertake between lifetimes, the origin of existence. The man knelt before her feet and cried out:
>
> "Oh, great mistress. Please help me. My life is miserable. Everywhere I go, I feel discomfort. Regardless of where I travel, I find no peace. I wander from town to town—and in no place do I find lasting rest. Please, bestow upon me your wisdom and make my life a joy again."
>
> The teacher smiled and gently touched his chin, lifting him from the ground. She said, "I can answer your query, my son. But first, I want you to go to a cave high up in the mountains—it's a place where I go to meditate when I need to escape the world and turn within. Stay there for forty nights—and by the end of that time, your question will have been answered."
>
> The man did as the guru requested. He packed a bag and trekked up the rocky terrain. It took a full day for him to find the cave—and during that time, he was

chased by a tiger, hissed at by snakes, and nipped at by bugs. He staggered in, ready to collapse. Curling up on the mistress's cot, he immediately fell asleep and dreamed of vibrant, swirling shapes.

The next day, he paced the cave anxiously. "When will the guru answer my question?" he wondered. From time to time, he would try to sit in meditation—but he was too agitated. His mind just spun in circles.

Frustrated and feeling unsuccessful, he got up and paced some more. One of the guru's disciples brought him a simple lunch and departed with a serene gaze. Feeling guilty that he hadn't yet made any progress in unraveling the nature of his unhappiness—he guiltily took the food, waved in thanks to the barer, and ate it all. He again tried to contemplate his question—but all he felt were waves of agitation, disappointment, and anger rolling through him. He cursed his fate and wondered why he had to suffer so. Why couldn't the teacher just answer him directly?

And so it continued for the next forty days. The man would try to better understand himself, feel his agitation heighten because he was getting nowhere, and eventually go to bed in a worse state than prior. As he slept, the vivid, curling colors would again fill his dreams—but he never remembered them when he awoke. Soon, the day had arrived to come down the mountain. Sadder than ever, he crawled into the abode of the teacher and wept on the floor before her.

"Tell me, young man—what did you learn during your forty nights in the cave?" she asked.

"Oh, guru," the man said in anguish, "I am such a failure. I wasted all that time. I had no profound revelations—I gained no insights as to my unhappiness. You said you would send me an answer—but I have failed you. I found none."

"You have not failed me, my son," the guru replied. The ancient-looking woman, with her paper-thin skin, delicately grabbed hold of a fan beside her and tapped the man on the top of the head. "You know the answers to the questions you sought."

In that instant, the same swirling rainbow of colors that greeted him every night during sleep swept the man out of his body. He swam through cosmic streams of interstellar light—he became one with all existence. He recognized that the dancing lights that made up his body were the same sparks igniting all of creation—he was one and the same as everything else in the known and unknown universe.

After days (or mere seconds) in this space beyond time, the man came back to himself, tears of intense bliss overflowing his eyelids. He understood that the knowledge he sought—knowledge of his true self—had always existed inside of him—he just hadn't realized it. He felt the pervasive joy of interconnectedness—a sameness with everything else in creation. How had he ever forgotten his truth, he wondered?

The guru continued to smile knowingly. "When you first came here, I could have answered you directly, but you would not have understood. Even though your time on the mountain felt unproductive, by sitting with your frustration, connecting with your longing, you opened doors inside of yourself. You had all this inside all along—your discomfort provided the key for you to finally unlock the bolts. You are ready now."

The teacher stared into his eyes—and he stared back. And without saying another word, the man understood. The man thanked the teacher, returned to his family and home, and lived a happy life. From then on, townspeople would refer to him as the radiant man on the mountain—the man who had seen God.

All this time, we've been trying to explore who we really are. But that "who" doesn't really exist. Because, who are you at your core? Both nothing and everything.

Ecstatic poets across time have tried to put this into words—but none have succeeded. Rumi might say, "We are stars wrapped in skin. The light you are seeking has always been within." Paulo Coelho might offer, "We are travelers on a cosmic journey, stardust, swirling and dancing in the eddies and whirlpools of infinity. Life is eternal. We have stopped for a moment to encounter each other, to meet, to love, to share." I might add, "You are star-shine made flesh. You are mortal, yet timeless. You are everywhere and nowhere—nothing more or less than the energy of creation manifested in physical form. A fragment of consciousness on its journey toward rediscovering its innate wholeness."

How do we put into words that which is unspeakable? This knowledge of your true self that you have been seeking has always been inside of you—waiting for you to rediscover it. You are already the bearer of your complete wholeness—you have never lost anything. You have simply forgotten your already perfected state. You are whole, you are beautiful, you simply have clouds blocking the radiance of your inner truth.

Who are you? You are a particular materialization of the same cosmic energy that has made everything else in creation. I think it can be helpful to examine the origin stories for why the universe came into existence, according to several esoteric faith traditions—because it is the same reason you are reading this book. Across civilizations, the same stories have reoccurred, claiming that cosmos exists for one particular reason—the pure joy of rediscovering its true self, one's divine nature. I will articulate this tale as best as I am able to understand it, given my own experiences and limited perspectives.

> *In the beginning, there was unmanifested consciousness—energy without form. At some point, that cosmic power split in half—unmoving awareness and a mobile, creative force. These two parts experienced such joy in being able to recognize itself—to feel the intense bonds*

of love with itself—that it split and diversified again. By differentiating, it got to know the immense joy of wholeness. So it split, and split, and split, and split. This is what scientists call the Big Bang—a sudden, explosive expansion of power from a single point into trillions of star systems, galaxies, and universes.

The movable, creative force of the cosmic intelligence so loved the experience of separating from itself—and the ensuing, orgasmic joy of reunification—that it kept dividing and creating, knowing that (at some point) each speck of itself would rejoin the whole and know inexpressible joy. She created planets and orbits, water and sky, plants and animals. She created polar opposites: day and night, positive and negative, masculine and feminine.

Soon, she was manifesting as quadrillions of living, respirating creatures. As she continued to diversify, some elements of herself forgot their true natures. They forgot that they were the pure, cosmic force of creation. But, ultimately, it did not matter—because the more thoroughly they forgot, the greater the bliss they would feel when they rediscovered their true selves.

And so it came to be that half of the cosmic truth remained unmoving—and the other half took physical form as known creation. Over time, the creative, ambulatory power lived every lifetime, experienced every state of being, and eventually longed to return to its source. After expanding outwards over billions of years, the universe contracted back in on itself, until it again became one, undifferentiated point of consciousness—one, infinitesimally small dot of unmanifested life-force. It stayed that way until—again—it desired the experience of reconnection. It then manifested life anew—splitting into its infinitely varied forms. A universe expanding and unfolding.

This spark of longing inside to know yourself is holy—it is why you exist. You came here, chose this life, because you desire to know yourself at your core. To truly come home to "you." By digging deeper inside, you begin to realize that there is no end to your internal search. The deeper you dig, the more you uncover that there is just layer upon layer of experiences, of accumulated identity. We are like onions—skin upon sheet of skin. If we are always looking for superficial qualities of who "I am," we will always be searching.

This is why our identities are always in flux. No matter how you describe yourself—even if it feels perfectly accurate at that moment—such descriptions will feel insufficient after a time. You'll think, "Well, that's not *entirely* me...I know more about myself now—I've dug deeper. I am actually different than I originally supposed." And then we relabel ourselves—never realizing that this is a never-ending process. There is always a next layer of the onion to peel, a deeper self-understanding to actualize.

There is no "knowable" you—there is only the unknowable. And that search for you is your spiritual quest. By turning our awareness to the core of our hearts, we explore the unshifting truth of who we really are—and in that search, we uncover our ancestral origins. We discern that we are the same energy that created the sky, the ground, the planets; we are the source of all. And by coming to understand our true nature, we will experience the immense bliss of reconnecting with our astral self. We will realize that we are part of the great "I am."

The third law of thermodynamics says that "energy cannot be created or destroyed—it can only be transmuted." So too is it with consciousness—self-aware energy. It just goes on and on—from form to form. Chemically-bound energy inside food transmutes into adenosine triphosphate inside your mitochondria and is used to power your cells. Solar energy transforms inside the chloroplasts of leaves to create simple sugars from which the plant builds new stems. Wood becomes light and heat when a log is set ablaze. Life is always converting energy from one form to another.

Einstein expanded on this idea with his famous formula: $E=mc^2$.

Simply put, physical matter (m) can be converted to energy (E) and back again when multiplied by the speed of light, squared. This is the same notion inherent within reincarnation—our cosmic sense of self transmutes from one physical structure to another, lifetime after lifetime. We arrive on Earth with so many accumulated memories, opinions, and perceptions because we have had countless previous existences. We have transitioned from flesh to spirit and back countless times. We are soulful travelers in a human body, here for the experience of learning our karmic lessons and discovering the immense pleasure in rediscovering our cosmic identity.

> *"You are the universe in ecstatic motion."*
> **— Rumi, Sufi poet and scholar**

One of my favorite words to describe the quality of our innate selves comes from the Indian subcontinent. It is a Sanskrit term: *satchitanada*—which is actually an amalgamation of three smaller words. They are: *sat* (truth), *chit* (consciousness), and *ananda (ecstatic bliss)*. At our core, according to this idea, we are all beings of inherent and unchanging truth, pure awareness, and ecstatic elation. When we fully recognize our essence and come back to our depths—that is what each of us will experience.

Truth—it is an idea that is challenging to pin down in the context of the modern world. One person can have a truth that is in direct opposition to another's—and yet, they can be equally valid. Two people passing by can witness the same happening and then walk away with two entirely separate memories.

The truth that *sat* is referring to is a truth even beyond objectivity. It is a truth that is always there—regardless of who witnesses it. The ancient *rishis*, or seers of long-ago times, said that if you delved deep into the landscape of the self, you would emerge with the same truth as everyone else. There is a truth to existence that is accessible to anyone at any time.

People tend to get so caught up in the differences that separate our perceptions—rather than our commonalities. There is an old parable of a group of blind men touching an elephant. One person feels the creature's trunk, another its leg, another its tail. Each of them articulates the truth they feel—a truth that is equally as valid as what any of the other men provide—yet they are totally unique. Despite their differences, however, each man is describing the same elephant. The elephant doesn't change—just our interpretation of it does.

So is it within ourselves. Faith and contemplative traditions across time have described our essence in countless ways. Some call it soul, others spirit. Some refer to it as *atman*, or *Bhrama*, or *ka*. It is the same divinity within each of us—a conscious awareness that observes and watches each action that takes place in our lives. This is the *chit* in *satchitananda*—a witness. An observer of the happenings of life. Descartes famously said, "I think, therefore I am." The fact that we are cognizant of being alive is a fundamental quality of our existence.

We tend to have a limited conception of who is entitled to be dubbed "conscious." It wasn't until very recent times—the past few decades, really—that most Americans came to view animals as being sentient creatures that experience pain, anguish, love, devotion, and separation. Before then, we viewed pets as objects. I've heard stories about how families in the 1950s would euthanize their dogs because they were going on vacation for a few weeks and didn't bother with finding a sitter. Animals were not given the same rights regarding their sentience and ability to feel as we now prescribe them—though many American state laws still don't protect pets' wellbeing. Animals are still legally dubbed property rather than conscious beings.

We don't have to go much further back—only to the Victorian era—to find children described in not too different of a way—as being insentient furniture taking up space. And—not too long before that—women were hailed similarly. A woman was bought and sold for the price of a dowry—once married, she became the property of her husband. Her feelings were not a matter of societal importance.

In contrast, various indigenous, folk, and shamanic traditions have recognized that every object in creation possesses pure awareness.

293

Not only animals—but plants and rocks, too. Anything in the tangible world has a spiritual component and a consciousness in and of itself. If you want to see proof of this, consider exploring the work of Dr. Monica Gagliano at the University of Western Australia and the University of Sydney. She studies how plants communicate (audibly and through chemical triggers), demonstrate sentience of their own, and are able to biologically respond to situational circumstances.[2] She is actively using science to understand how awareness can exist beyond the narrow bounds that Western people have typically established for it to exist within.

The last third of the word is *ananda*—rapturous bliss. Some traditions equate the joy of being rooted in one's self to the most heightened sexual ecstasy imaginable—ten thousand orgasms burbling at once. Think of the emotions we most actively seek out in life: joy, happiness, satisfaction, euphoria. It's why people take pharmaceutical pills and jump out of airplanes. It's why we eat food, take naps, make love. We are creatures that seek bliss and avoid pain—it is hardwired into our brains. It is the first experience our cells knew, back when we were zygotes. When sperm met egg, our parents knew bliss.

When one considers the act of creating new life—it is often an act of ecstasy. Most of us are created out of bliss; it is the emotion that surrounded us at the moment of conception. It is why loving another person feels so meaningful—we are meant to dwell in love, to marinate in it. We constantly seek that which is our intrinsic nature and move away from its opposite. We seek pleasure, seek love, and avoid pain.

Church road signs across the country proclaim "God is love"— but few actually consider the reality of that phrase. The force that powered the stars and established life on earth—is the same force that you feel when you connect with your ecstatic self. That same energy fills your core—the very center point in the middle of the proverbial onion. Your "self" is pure joy and ecstatic radiance.

Vajrayana Buddhist and Shaivite Tantric traditions depict deities in the throes of lovemaking because that intense bliss is the same force that ignited the Big Bang, that created your body when your parents conjugally joined. That is why orgasms feel so good—they remind us of our innate state of transversal being. The love of the universe in intercourse with itself is the bliss that lights up the truth inside your heart.

Hindus describe a tiny, mustard-size *bindu* in our energetic middle—a singularity point of ecstasy, joy, and radiant love. This is who you truly are. You are love, you are truth, you are awareness, you are bliss, you are the same force that we describe as being the almighty—because the almighty is, at its essence—also all of these things. God is love—love is God. There is no difference between you. That energy is also the seat you are sitting on, the neighbor beside you, and the plant you ate as dinner last night. You are everything and nothing—this corporeal shell that you walk around in is simply a beautiful mechanism that is not you, but also *is* you. It is all the same life force.

Do you see why I asked if you would be willing to set aside logic and enter a realm of the ineffable with me? We are taking this exploration of self into a whole other dimension. I felt that it was important to include this topic in *Journey to the Ecstatic Self* because it is the ultimate question. Who are we *really*, at our innermost cores? If we keep following the footpaths that consider the question of selfhood, we will eventually have to step into the realms of the esoteric and spiritual. There is only so much that can be addressed on the firm footing of quantifiable reality. To get to the core of our truths, we have to move past the pure logic and enter the dimension beyond space. We have to be willing to shrug off our mortal flesh and examine the timeless qualities that are the root of our experiences.

You were put here to know your "self" in its entirety. It is why you are reading this book, why you are on this journey. There are many different types of paths that lead to the soul—and the one I've been sharing with you is only one of quintillions. It is not the only way—nor is it by any means the best—it is simply the one I am walking and am able to share. But we are all on the same journey—even those of us who wouldn't seem in the least spiritual. We are all on the road toward home—even if we don't recognize it, even if we appear to be actively working to move in the opposite direction. We are all creatures of spirit moving toward reconnection, and the more that you can embrace the notion that some of your questions won't necessarily have logical answers, the greater peace you will find with being where you are.

Because, where you are is perfect. You are exactly where you need to be. In fact, there is nowhere else you *can* be because...well, you are where you are. There's no denying your current point of geography. We need to appreciate that we don't have a clear vantage as to the course of our own path. In the parable I shared earlier in this chapter—about the man seeking the teachings of the guru—he thought he was in the depths of his own despair. He thought he was lost, hopelessly confused, and going nowhere. He spent forty nights in the cave and believed that he was making zero progress. All the while, dreams were visiting him, sharing the truth of his identity—he just couldn't recognize it.

So it is within us all. We don't realize how close we might be to our own spontaneous realization. Your "coming home" to your true, cosmic self, might happen in the very next breath. You might have already gotten all the lessons you've needed to learn and are just waiting to be bonked on the head so you know your truth. This is why we should never compare our path to another's—we are all on different steps, exploring different vantages, and heading different directions. Who's to say if someone is further along than another? We are all perfect precisely where we are.

We already are the complete, love-filled selves that the ancient spiritual traditions describe—those realized states are within us. We each just have lifetimes of debris blocking us from that knowledge. But, one day, those clouds will part, and you will suddenly remember your enlightened nature. You already have everything you need inside of you—that "self" that is you is already healed, radiant, and whole. You are *satchitanda*. You are *atman*. You are soul. The Christian trinity describes God as being the "Father, Son, and Holy Ghost"—that third one is what exists inside your heart. Go there and dwell.

MEDITATION XV

Meditation traditions across time have highlighted the idea of energetic bodies—or patterns of life-force pulsing within. I would like to invite you to become acquainted with your elemental self, which is connected to, but separate from, your corporeal form.

Close your eyes and bring your focus down to the bottom of your pelvis. This area is your energetic root—some call it the *mulandara chakra*. It is the area of your survival instincts, your grounding onto our planet. Its element is that of earth—heavy, dense. Envision a deep, blood-red color traveling down and out of you, spreading like roots into the floor. This is your connection to sustenance, to this earthly plane.

If you move to the insertion point of your genitals, here is your sexual and emotional core. The *svadishthana chakra*. It is an area of water—of movement. Feel your essence, your emotional self, moving here, swirling around. Feel your vitality, your inner force of creation. Breathe into this orange, glowing space and flow with the energy of creation. Sexuality is inherently fluid—these sexual organs expel liquid when aroused.

Up a little higher, around your navel, is the wheel of fire—the *maripurna chakra*. This is your energetic core—it is a brilliant, golden light that shines out and around you. It protects you; it propels your agency into the world. When you wish to manifest a project or a goal—this is where you draw from. When you want to establish personal boundaries, this is where you pull. It is a fire burning in your belly, ready to set the world ablaze.

To the middle of your chest—the heart center—is the *anahatha chakra*. Emerald in color, it is the seat of love, the seat of compassion. Cosmic identity exists here. If you ask some cultures where their self exists—they will point to their hearts. It is where we connect with others for whom we care about—it is a center of devotion. It is also the nexus point between the lower, earth-bound chakras, and the higher, more etheric ones. Its element is air—it fills the space between. We are creatures of both heaven and earth—traveling in between—neither entirely animal nor fully astral being. We are spiritual creatures having a bodily experience, and we are centered here. Feel the love in this space. Feel home.

Near the base of your neck is the *vishudda chakra*—the nexus point of ether or empty space. It is the place of our cosmic expression, our voice, and our intuitive abilities. Deep blue in color, dreams live in this chakra—self-expression happens here. When we connect with this space, we experience vastness and connection with all living beings. Actively swallowing can allow a sense of opening here.

To the space between and slightly above our eyebrows, we go next. This is the *anja chakra*—the third eye. A light bluish-purple in color—here, we see what is not visible with the naked eye. We have moved beyond elements—there is no air, water, fire, ether, or earth to sense here—we are pure awareness. This is where psychic abilities manifest—the ability to witness that which is not visible. The tantric god Shiva is often depicted with his third eye open—for he observes all. He is the realized yogic master. Enlightened and reposing in the true self. Dwell here with him.

At the top of the head is the *sahasrara chakra*—the crown energy center. Our connection to the divine. Through this nexus, we experience the higher realms. We access our spiritual ancestry, our astral DNA. Feel a purple or pure white pervading light surrounding you, enveloping you—as if a brilliant, white sun were shining just above the top of your head. Here, we experience cosmic unification and nothingness. God is everything—everything is a manifestation of God. We are pure, holy, perfected, and splendid. Dwell in this knowledge and sense your connection with all.

When you are done, run up and down the core of your being—the central channel connecting all of these chakras together. Feel them working in harmony. Feel how you are a child of earth, water, fire, air, ether, and spirit. You are all of these divine, spinning wheels—and so much more. Feel your radiance. Feel your light. Feel your indestructible worth as a child of the divine.

Om.

> *"Your task is not to seek for love, but merely to seek and find all the barriers within yourself that you have built against it."*
> — **Rumi, Sufi poet and mystic scholar**

If you are like many individuals in contemporary life who feel like discussing spiritual matters is uncomfortable, my apologies to you. Many of us have grown up in religious faiths that have pushed us further away from our innate truths—hypocrisy, excessive dogma, and intentional shaming happen within too many spiritual traditions, driving a wedge between people and their innate essences. I encourage you to question why you believe what you believe—let go of anything that you've been taught that feels inauthentic—and turn your focus within. The ancient seers say that, if you do, you will find your reality. You will experience—for yourself—what I have attempted to relate in this chapter. You will find you.

I was raised as a part of the Methodist Church. I enjoyed the prayers, the celebrations through song, the pageantry. But I longed for a deeper understanding of spirituality—a more personal relationship with God (and the ecstatic force of creation) than the church could provide. This is why, in college, I set my sights to the East. It's the principal reason I moved into an ashram and undertook intense practices like spending three hours in meditation each sunrise for eight years—I longed to know my truth. I longed to reunite with my quintessential self.

I don't think that any one tradition holds all the answers—nor do I believe that anyone should have to leave the faith in which they were raised in order to know their esoteric depths. There are beautiful explorations into mysticism within every tradition—Kabbalah in Judaism, Gnostic or Desert Father sects in Christianity, Vajrayana or Bön in Buddhism, Shaivite Tantra in Hinduism, to name a few. We need to explore what inspires us, steal from the best, and be open to growth.

One of the issues I found with my upbringing—that I think is common to many raised in a Christian faith—is the notion of "sin." For me, the notion of some unnegotiable wrong that could forever damn me seemed antithetical to Christ's teachings of love. His messages of forgiveness, humility, graciousness, and compassion didn't seem to match how the church described our inherent natures. We were told we were broken, separated from God, permanently stained. Inherently sinful. I didn't resonate with that. I saw each person as a beautiful fraction of the divine. That's why, converting to Eastern spirituality, I was delighted to encounter non-dualistic thinking. A sense that we all are inherently good, perfected, and unified with divine consciousness. There was no all-knowing God in opposition to sinful me—there was just a continuous divine energy flowing through and forming everything.

In fact, sin was never meant to be part of Jesus' message in the way the contemporary church currently says it is. The notion of sin as we think of it today didn't come into play until the Council of Trent in the 16th century. Before then, the actual meaning of the word—in the original, Aramaic language—was "an arrow missing the mark."[3] That's all. A misguided action. It wasn't something negative or evil—something for which a person needs to atone or feel guilty. Certainly not something for which to suffer hellfire and brimstone. It was just an action a person undertook that was not aligned with their best interests. Something that could be easily changed next time—that maybe slightly separated them from their inner truth. It wasn't even qualified as being bad—it was just misguided.

By contrast, in the modern world, the word has been imbued with anger, disconnection, shame, and hatred. We have made sin a permanent, criminal offense that damns a person. It has led many to separate themselves from themselves—to become fragmented people. They reject parts of themselves that seem incongruous, that seem sinful, and thereby become half-people. It's impossible to feel like we truly belong and are worthy of being loved in our entirety when we hold parts of our identity as broken or unworthy. We cannot accept our full selves when certain aspects are deemed "sinful." Instead, we need to adopt a vantage that sees each part of ourselves as holy. We are inherently good, sacred, and beautiful beings of spirit. We need to overcome the misguided lessons we've been taught and see our inherent perfection. We are whole.

Let go of thinking there is anything wrong with you. You are exactly where you should be, as you should be. Right here and now—you are already radiant. You are already perfected. You are magnificent. When you can fully accept this notion, to see yourself in your truth—you will know bliss. You will know your worth. You will know the oneness of creation. You will become unified with the cosmic all.

Do your best—forgive easily. Know your inner light—your spiritual truth. Live for something meaningful. Strive to connect with your deepest self. If you succeed, I guarantee you will find a sense of home, of belonging with yourself and others. You will know the radiant spirit that is you. You will love and celebrate your ecstatic self.

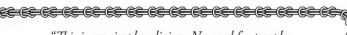

> *"This is my simple religion. No need for temples.*
> *No need for complicated philosophy.*
> *Your own mind, your own heart is the temple.*
> *Your philosophy is simple kindness."*
> — **His Holiness, the Fourteenth Dalai Lama,**
> **spiritual leader**

SUMMARY:

— Live for something greater than yourself—it doesn't matter what: a mission, a cause, a person, an animal. Let your life be bigger than just you.

— Search inside for an understanding of your true essence—it is something that is more profound than just identity. This is the stuff of soul.

— Seek a vantage of being timeless, whole, and perfected. Any thing that tells you that you're less-than is a roadblock to be dismantled.

Epilogue:

THE ROAD HOME

Whew. That's it—the end of the path. You've made it.
How do you feel? Breathless?
I hope the answer is, "Good. Well. Better adjusted."
I hope so—because, if it hasn't already...your life is about to radically shift.

You've made it to the trail's end, the proverbial mountain top. Now you've got to climb back down and integrate everything you've learned.

"Once you know better, do better," said Maya Angelou. Now you know—and you can never go back.

You can never go back to those toxic relationships that make you feel small. You can never go back to pretending you don't know exactly what you're worth. You can never go back to accepting poor behavior toward yourself from yourself—or from anyone else. You cannot go back to enduring those mindless friendships that pull you further away from authenticity. You can't go back to that car that you secretly hate but bought because you thought it would help you get laid. You can't go back. Ever.

Once you know better, you do better. You make different choices.

You may find yourself, over the coming days, spending less and less time around friends that drain you; you may find yourself browsing online sites for a new career; you may find yourself spending time in nature or by large bodies of water, drawing on the healing power of the organic world. You may find yourself seeking quiet and solace more often or spending time with animals. You may find yourself avoiding crowds and loud, chaotic environments.

All of that is okay. It may be scary to experience change—but it's part of the landscape ahead. We live many lifetimes within one lifespan if we are growing and learning. The person you will be tomorrow is not who you were last week, and our surroundings have to change to reflect that inner evolution.

You can always love someone from your past from a distance; you can always bless them and send them positive vibes. You may even find you still have reason to enjoy their company for different reasons (as I've gotten older, some of my childhood friends have become my most dear relationships), but they have to be people who are willing to see you anew, willing to allow you to evolve and mature. Those who hold you tightly within a box of expectations, those who demand that you respond in the same old ways and want the same old things—they won't survive your inner transitions.

So, my apologies: this journey toward ecstatic selfdom may have ruined your current life. You can never go back to the way things were now that you know what's on the other side of this veil of self-awareness. Because now that you know, you'll never be able to forget it. You can assuredly try to bury the self-knowledge you've attained, but it'll haunt your dreams. It'll send prickles to your belly that shout, "This isn't you—you are aware of who you really are—you know what you need to be doing."

We've shattered your status-quo—but I won't apologize because I know from personal experience it *needed* to happen. I had to cut through and climb out of the chrysalis. Each time my life has blown up, each time I've gone through a dramatic personal change—especially an incredibly *painful* one—life gets so much better. It can take time for the dust to settle, even years—but once it does, the sky will be so much clearer than it was prior. You will feel freer, more integrated, and more authentically *you*. I've lost relationships, but I've gained myself. I've lost friends and career opportunities, but I've found a self-understanding that has been far more validating than any external source could have ever been. And, once we have accepted ourselves, the people and life necessities/experiences that will be the most supportive and beneficial to our new outlook will find us naturally.

So, this is my advice to you: take what you can use from this book and leave what you can't. Whatever exercises I've given you that assist you on your journey—use them. Enjoy them. Make them your own. If something I shared doesn't speak to you—leave it behind. I won't be offended. Learn to see each person you meet as a direction-giver—they have been walking their path and might have something of value to offer you on yours. No one is a perfect guide, so use what you find to be helpful, but don't think you need to carry everything with you.

You now have a robust set of tools to reorient you to your truest self. I encourage you to explore this book to the depth of your abilities and find what in it makes the best sense for your specific situations in life. I encourage you to delve into self-understanding as an unending quest—the more you learn about yourself, the more you realize that there is much yet to learn. Approach your coming-into-wholeness with a sense of curiosity, a sense of play, and a sense of wild delight. Realize that this is a lifetime-long journey—and that there is no final destination. When we have reached the hills of self-belonging—there are even more fantastic mountains on the horizon.

It has been a sincere pleasure and honor to walk with you for a few steps along your path. On my website (ecstaticself.com), I share further resources that have inspired me on my journey—and may do the same for you. Everyone is a potential teacher—say thank you to those who inspire you, as well as those who show you who you do not want to be. Try to find the sacred in everything—and remind yourself that you are connected to so much more than the limits of your physical body.

We are all on this adventure together—and I look forward to meeting you at another crossroads, in this life or the next.

Safe travels, my friend. May your ways be safe and prosperous until we encounter one another again. Be brave. Be bold. Go with your truth and bliss.

The truth in me bows to the truth in you—inside, we are one.

RESOURCES

Private Coaching

If you enjoyed *Journey to the Ecstatic Self* and would like to collaborate with Kae in one-on-one sessions, he provides private life coaching through his business, Ecstatic Self. Offerings range from a twelve-week transformation journey to a shorter four-week introduction to meditation. More information can be found at ecstaticself.com.

Video Lessons

On his YouTube channel, Ecstatic Self, Kae offers short, daily videos that more deeply explore the topics addressed in this book. Subscribe at youtube.com/ecstaticself.

Retreats and Workshops

Kae leads workshops globally on compassion, connection, intimacy, and belonging. Please visit ecstaticself.com for an updated list of current and upcoming offerings.

Audio Lessons

Recordings of the meditations found in *Journey to the Ecstatic Self* can be found at ecstaticself.com/meditations—and a *free* download of the audiobook can be accessed at audible.com when you select the "30-day free trial." Kae will also be launching a podcast available on all streaming services.

Further Reading

Please visit ecstaticself.com for a list of suggested books, articles, and materials that have inspired Kae and his personal growth journey. He regularly publishes his own, shorter material on medium.com/@ecstaticself.

ACKNOWLEDGMENTS

F irst and foremost, my darling husband, Anthony—with whom, anything is possible. Thank you for your tireless encouragement, support, and eternal love. I am grateful for being your #foreverfriend.

Thank you to my artistic collaborators: Kayli Baker for making my words sound better than they would have on their own; Alfred Obare and Predra6 for your staggeringly beautiful design work; Tuan Bui for your awesome author picture. Sarah L. Carnes and Rick Buell for catching errors invisible to my eyes. Y'all make me look prettier than I actually am.

My sources of inspiration:

This project flashed into my head on a night of fasting, celebrating Mahashivaratri, the holiday of Lord Shiva. I credit you for the inspiration and direction this book has taken. *Om Namah Shivaya*—we are all one. Gratitude and glory to the divine within and without!

To John Garnett—you were my sounding board, the first to read my rambling first drafts. Thank you for inspiring me to realize how needed a book like this is. To Robert Millar—for being the first man to boldly walk this path with me as a spiritual life coach. Thank you for being a trailblazer.

To all the many teachers I've had on my journey. To David Edelfelt and his husband, Anthony. You were my first gay mentor. You showed me how to live as an emphatically authentic, connected, and spiritually attuned man. To Bob Scogin, rest his soul. All those hours of pounding Shakespeare in my head were about so much more than just verse structure and the Bard, my wise, old friend. To Dr. Talavane Krishna—you have the sweetest, most bodhisattvic energy of anyone I've known. You've taught me to relax into my spirituality and deepen inside. To Linda Callanan—you who provide masterful guidance and see the writings in the heavens. You have encouraged mine and Anthony's life to blossom in ways richer than we dreamed. To Ricky Hall—my crazy, psychic friend. Thanks for holding me accountable and exploring the mysteries of the universe with me. To Minita Gandhi, my soul sister. Namaste, my beloved lady.

To the men along my path who have taught me about myself. Seyi, Keven, Jason, Nathan, Ryan, Shiv—not all of our stories ended happily, but each of you left me with gifts: a richer understanding of myself, an appreciation of tender connection, the power of vulnerability, and an eagerness for growth. You have all been my teachers.

To the people at the ashram—Jim & Faith, Kat & Zach, Mandy, Anna, Jan & Jon, John & Susan, Rachel, Sheila, Laurie & Oliver, Jennifer, Paula, and all the dozens of others. Though we may not speak again, I still hold gratitude for you. Together, we shared countless magical experiences and sleepless nights throwing grains of rice into sacred fires. May you thrive and prosper.

For the teachers who I've never met in person but have taught me immensity: Elizabeth Lesser, Alan Downs, Brené Brown, the incomparable Mary Shmich, Hannah Gadsby, Johann Hari, Howard Y. Lee, Lorin Roche, Lao Tzu, Rupaul Charles, Patanjali, Mahatma Gandhi, His Holiness the Dalai Lama, Geshe Tenzin Wangyal Rinpoche, Nelson Mandela, Dr. Nida Chenagtsang, Lars Muhl, Ben Joffe, Vasant Lad, Daniel Goleman, Paulo Coelho, David Frawley, Robert Svoboda, Bhagavan Nityananda, Dr. Martin Luther King Jr., Rumi, Oriah Mountain Dreamer, Georg Feuerstein, Haruki Murakami, JK Rowling, Robert Jordan, Garth Stein, Miyuki Miyabe, Elizabeth Gilbert, Miss William Shakespeare, Elizabeth Warren, and the countless others who have made impressions on my soul with your beautiful thoughts, mantras, words, and prayers.

For my dear Pleionidys. Thank you, always.

To those beautiful souls who have shown me kindness, shared your stories, bared your hearts as you've responded to my work online. I see you; I hold you. Thank you for carrying me this far. To my clients who teach me through your gracious resilience, your tenacity for growth—you are my mentors.

To my parents. You've never once flagged in your belief that I could accomplish anything to which I set my mind—you've been my biggest champions and cheerleaders always. Thank you for being my first gurus and the best mom and dad a soul could ask to have. I have been so blessed by being your son.

For my grandmother—you, who are still with me in spirit, have shown me what selfless love truly means. To my extended family—all my crazy, colorful relatives who have made me feel cherished. To my brothers, Mark & Mike, and our soulful conversations. To my adopted family, Carmen & Rob, Alex & Rhea, Elizabeth & Michael. To my chosen family: the wonderful friends who support me, answer my cascade of text messages, and remind me of the real purpose of living—sharing joy with others. Matt & Kate, Kristi, Michael, Dan, Alex, Taylor, Kendell & Lisa, Michelle & Zach, Katie, Sarah, Ben, Jordan & Arielle, Felicia, Jamil & Malik, Ricky, Connor, Cara & David, Alyssa & Brad...just to shout out to a few in particular. Thank you.

To the undoubtedly dozens (or hundreds) of others whom I have forgotten. You're still in my heart!

REFERENCES

2. Serene Vistas Ahead

1. Marshall, R. (2015, September 10). How Many Ads Do You See in One Day? Retrieved July 11, 2020, from https://www.redcrow-marketing.com/2015/09/10/many-ads-see-one-day/

2. Weiss, A. (2018). Comment on Wilson et al. (2014). Just think: The challenges of the disengaged mind. Science, 345, 75-77. *Science Magazine, 345(6192)*, 75-77. doi:10.31234/osf.io/7ngm2

3. CMUScience. (2012, June 11). Who's stressed in the US? Carnegie Mellon researchers study adult stress levels from 1983-2009. Retrieved July 11, 2020, from http://www.eurekalert.org/pub_releases/2012-06/cmu-wsi061112.php

4. Hölzel, B. K., Carmody, J., Vangel, M., Congleton, C., Yerramsetti, S. M., Gard, T., Lazar, S. W. (2011). Mindfulness practice leads to increases in regional brain gray matter density. *Psychiatry Research: Neuroimaging*, 191(1), 36-43. doi:10.1016/j.pscychresns.2010.08.006

5. Doidge, N. (2017). *The brain's way of healing: Remarkable discoveries and recoveries from the frontiers of neuroplasticity*. Brunswick, Victoria: Scribe.

6. Adluru, N., Korponay, C. H., Norton, D. L., Goldman, R. I., Da-

vidson, R. J. (2020). BrainAGE and regional volumetric analysis of a Buddhist monk: A longitudinal MRI case study. *Neurocase, 26(2)*, 79-90. doi:10.1080/13554794.2020.1731553

7. Gallegos, A. M., Crean, H. F., Pigeon, W. R., Heffner, K. L. (2017). Meditation and yoga for posttraumatic stress disorder: A meta-analytic review of randomized controlled trials. *Clinical Psychology Review, 58*, 115-124. doi:10.1016/j.cpr.2017.10.004

8. Maybin, S. (2017, March 10). Busting the attention span myth. Retrieved July 11, 2020, from https://www.bbc.com/news/health-38896790

9. Wong, K. (2015, July 29). How Long It Takes to Get Back on Track After a Distraction. Retrieved July 11, 2020, from https://lifehacker.com/how-long-it-takes-to-get-back-on-track-after-a-distract-1720708353

10. Wade, N. (Aug. 2, 2005). Your Body is Younger Than You Think. *The New York Times.* Retrieved July 11, 2020, from http://www.nytimes.com/2005/08/02/science/02cell.html?pagewanted=all

11. Naik, R., Shrivastava, S., Suryawanshi, H., & Gupta, N. (2019). Microchimerism: A new concept. *Journal of Oral and Maxillofacial Pathology*, 23(2), 311. doi:10.4103/jomfp.jomfp_85_17

12. Goleman, D., & Davidson, R. J. (2018). *Altered traits: Science reveals how meditation changes your mind, brain, and body.* NY, NY: Avery, an imprint of Penguin Random House LLC.

13. Bayes-Fleming, N., Delehanty, H., Staff, M., Boyce, B., Hanson, R., Begley, S., . . . Newman, K. (2018, September 18). The Remarkable Brains of Long-Term Meditators. Retrieved July 11, 2020, from https://www.mindful.org/the-remarkable-brains-of-high-level-meditators

14. Ma, X., Yue, Z., Gong, Z., Zhang, H., Duan, N., Shi, Y., . . . Li, Y. (2017). The Effect of Diaphragmatic Breathing on Attention, Negative Affect and Stress in Healthy Adults. *Frontiers in Psychology, 8*. doi:10.3389/fpsyg.2017.00874

15. Chronic stress puts your health at risk. (2019, March 19). Retrieved July 11, 2020, from https://www.mayoclinic.org/healthy-lifestyle/stress-management/in-depth/stress/art-20046037

16. Vagus nerve stimulation. (2018, December 07). Retrieved July 11, 2020, from https://www.mayoclinic.org/tests-procedures/vagus-nerve-stimulation/about/pac-20384565

17. Grill-Spector, K., Henson, R., & Martin, A. (2006). Repetition and the brain: Neural models of stimulus-specific effects. *Trends in Cognitive Sciences*, 10(1), 14-23. doi:10.1016/j.tics.2005.11.006

3. Steepening Curves

1. Denworth, L. (2019, June 13). How Much Time in Nature Is Needed to See Benefits? Retrieved July 11, 2020, from https://www.psychologytoday.com/us/blog/brain-waves/201906/how-much-time-in-nature-is-needed-see-benefits

4. Entering the Crevasse

1. Schulte, B. (2015, May 26). Harvard neuroscientist: Meditation not only reduces stress, here's how it changes your brain. Retrieved July 11, 2020, from https://www.washingtonpost.com/news/inspired-life/wp/2015/05/26/harvard-neuroscientist-meditation-not-only-reduces-stress-it-literally-changes-your-brain/

5. Rainbows and Peculiar Roads

1. Squeglia, L. M., Jacobus, J., & Tapert, S. F. (2014). The effect of alcohol use on human adolescent brain structures and systems. *Handbook of Clinical Neurology Alcohol and the Nervous System*, 501-510. doi:10.1016/b978-0-444-62619-6.00028-8

2. McCarthy, J. (2020, June 08). Americans Still Greatly Overestimate U.S. Gay Population. Retrieved July 11, 2020, from https://news.gallup.com/poll/259571/americans-greatly-overestimate-gay-population.aspx

3. Accord Alliance (n.d.). F1000 Commentary: Brain responses to sexual images in 46, XY women with complete androgen insensitivity syndrome are female typical. / How common are these

conditions? Retrieved July 11, 2020, from https://www.accordalliance.org/faqs/how-common-are-these-conditions/

4. Ballard, J. (2020, June 01). Is sexuality a spectrum? Americans aren't sure. Retrieved July 11, 2020, from https://today.yougov.com/topics/lifestyle/articles-reports/2020/06/01/sexuality-spectrum-pride-lgbtq-poll

5. Reuters. (2020, February 12). Suicide rates fall among gay youth but still outpace straight peers. Retrieved July 11, 2020, from https://www.nbcnews.com/feature/nbc-out/suicide-rates-fall-among-gay-youth-still-outpace-straight-peers-n1135141

6. Grab Your Climbing Buddy's Hand

1. Twenge, J., Joiner, T., & Rogers, M. (2019). Corrigendum: Increases in Depressive Symptoms, Suicide-Related Outcomes, and Suicide Rates Among U.S. Adolescents After 2010 and Links to Increased New Media Screen Time. *Clinical Psychological Science*, 7(2), 397-397. doi:10.1177/2167702618824060

2. Ballard, J. (2019, July 30). Millennials are the loneliest generation. Retrieved July 11, 2020, from https://today.yougov.com/topics/lifestyle/articles-reports/2019/07/30/loneliness-friendship-new-friends-poll-survey

3. University of Chicago. (2009, December 8). In cancer-ridden rats, loneliness can kill: Isolation and stress identified as contributing to breast cancer risk. *ScienceDaily*. Retrieved July 4, 2020 from www.sciencedaily.com/releases/2009/12/091207151222.htm

4. Dutton, J., Johnson, A., & Hickson, M. (2017). Touch Revisited: Observations and Methodological Recommendations. *Journal of Mass Communication & Journalism*, 07(05). doi:10.4172/2165-7912.1000348

5. Keltner, D. (n.d.). Hands On Research: The Science of Touch. Retrieved July 11, 2020, from https://greatergood.berkeley.edu/article/item/hands_on_research

6. Hari, J. (2019). *Lost connections: Why you're depressed and how to find hope.* London: Bloomsbury Publishing.

7. Tierney, R. (2018, April 11). The power of touch. Retrieved July 11, 2020, from https://www.telegraph.co.uk/beauty/skin/youthful-vitality/the-power-of-touch/

7. Sun's Out, Shirt's Off

1. Center for Disease Control (2020, June 29). Adult Obesity Facts. Retrieved July 11, 2020, from https://www.cdc.gov/obesity/data/adult.html

2. US Department of Justice. (n.d.). Steroid Abuse in Today's Society. Retrieved July 11, 2020, from https://www.deadiversion.usdoj.gov/pubs/brochures/steroids/professionals/

3. Bolding, G., Sherr, L., & Elford, J. (2002). Use of anabolic steroids and associated health risks among gay men attending London gyms. *Addiction*, 97(2), 195-203. doi:10.1046/j.1360-0443.2002.00031.x

4. Frontiers. (2019, April 4). Stressed? Take a 20-minute 'nature pill': Just 20 minutes of contact with nature will lower stress hormone levels, reveals new study. ScienceDaily. Retrieved July 11, 2020 from www.sciencedaily.com/releases/2019/04/190404074915.htm

5. Hedley, G. (Producer). (2009, February 7). *The Fuzz Speech* [Video file]. Retrieved July 7, 2020, from https://youtu.be/_FtSP-tkSug

8. Swapping Campfire Tales

1. Davidson, R. J., Kabat-Zinn, J., Schumacher, J., Rosenkranz, M., Muller, D., Santorelli, S. F., . . . Sheridan, J. F. (2003). Alterations in Brain and Immune Function Produced by Mindfulness Meditation. *Psychosomatic Medicine*, 65(4), 564-570. doi:10.1097/01.psy.0000077505.67574.e3

2. Elizabeth Scott, M. (2020, February 25). How to Reduce Negative Self-Talk for a Better Life. Retrieved July 11, 2020, from https://www.verywellmind.com/negative-self-talk-and-how-it-affects-us-4161304

3. Roche, L. (2017, August 17). Ep 1 Lorin Roche PhD - Guru Viking Interviews [Interview by S. James]. Retrieved July 7, 2020, from https://podcasts.apple.com/us/podcast/guru-viking-podcast/id1451432089?i=1000429052608

4. Cron, L. (2016). *Story genius: How to use brain science to go beyond outlining and write a riveting novel (before you waste three years writing 327 pages that go nowhere)*. Berkeley: Ten Speed Press.

10. Ascending the Spire

1. Barragan, R., Brooks, R., & Meltzoff, A. (2020, February 04). Altruistic food sharing behavior by human infants after a hunger manipulation. Retrieved July 11, 2020, from https://www.nature.com/articles/s41598-020-58645-9

2. Calvo P, Gagliano M , Souza GM & A Trewavas (2020) Plants are intelligent, and here is how. *Annals of Botany.* 125: 11–28. Retrieved July 11, 2020, from https://doi.org/10.1093/aob/mcz155

3. Muhl, L. (2014). *The law of light: The secret teachings of Jesus.* London: Watkins Publishing.

AUTHOR BIO

Kae is a storyteller, spiritual life coach, and performing artist. Originally from Chicago, he has taught yoga and meditation since 2008, lived in an ashram for seven years, and acted on stages and in media projects across the country. Globally, he has led workshops on mindfulness, connection, creativity, and empathy. He is a graduate of Northwestern University (*magna cum laude*) and currently resides in Washington, D.C. with his husband and rescue pup.

Kaestrouse.com
@kaestrouse

Made in the USA
Las Vegas, NV
23 November 2020